THEATRE AND EDUCATION

HUMAN HORIZONS SERIES

DISABILITY, THEATRE AND EDUCATION

Richard Tomlinson

A CONDOR BOOK
SOUVENIR PRESS (E&A) LTD

ISBN 0 285 64962 0 casebound
ISBN 0 285 649639 9 paperback

Photoset, printed and bound in Great Britain by
Redwood Burn Ltd
Trowbridge, Wiltshire

Contents

Acknowledgements

There are legions of people to thank for their support and belief in what Graeae was trying to do. In the early days it was Elizabeth Hargreaves and Michael and Maureen Silver who actually did something about getting the company going. Later on, members of the board such as Dr Robert Chivers, Jem Barnes and Andrew Bruce gave their time and effort without stint. In America Professor Tim Nugent and Eden Nicholas were unbelievably helpful and supportive. In this country a huge assortment of people have put themselves out to accommodate, feed and entertain the company. However, the real workers for Graeae have been the company themselves, and to all of them, past, present and future, my thanks. The following people have been members of the company:

Alex Low	Yvonne Allen
Will Kennen	Ellen Wilkie
Barbara Warren	Mandy Sprague
Jag Plah	Sue Bishop
Elane Roberts	Nic Fine
Mike Flower	Deniz Bulli
Maggie Woolley	Marion Saunders

and finally, my old friend Nabil Shaban, without whom the company would never have started.

I should also like to thank Methuen London Ltd. for permission to quote two passages from *The Dumb Waiter* by Harold Pinter.

Introduction

Jeff told me about his accident. He had gone to the seaside with his family and had decided to dive off the pier into the sea. What he did not know was that there were blocks of concrete just under the surface. He hit one. Here is an extract from his account as I rewrote it (under the title of *High Dive*, a twelve-minute monologue):

I broke my bloody neck doing that. Hysterical, isn't it? Absolutely bloody hysterical. I didn't know it – eighteen inches beneath the water were cement blocks supporting the pier. I couldn't see them 'cos they'd been painted blue to merge into the general marine set-up. So I hit one. Boing. (*He is laughing.*) I can remember it, you know. Distinctly. Quite distinctly. I remember floating on the water face down. All I was concerned with was not breathing. I had heard that breathing while face down in water was not beneficial to health. So I was dragged out and lay on the beach. I could see the sky – blue, clear – ideal day for diving off the pier. We'd all come down for the day, you know, mother, dad and our kid. I kept telling my father, 'Not to worry, not to worry.' His face was above me. Blotched red and white. And do you know he had a handkerchief knotted at the corners and he looked really scared. 'It's all right, Dad,' I kept saying. But I felt as though my arms were still hanging down in the water. I knew they couldn't be because I was on the sand. On the sand and my arms shouldn't be hanging down. (*Pause.*) The next bit is muddled. I remember a helicopter, which was exciting, and a weight pulling my head straight. They bore holes in your skull and hang weights from it. Horribly gruesome, isn't it? But I quite enjoyed the helicopter, and I went to hospital for ages, and what with physio, rehabilitation, occupational therapy, hydrotherapy, I've had hospital....

Let me tell you about the lavatory. That's good for a laugh and it's no good being offended because you all go. Don't you now? You get up, go to the lavatory, and so on. Dead easy. All well designed. Everything functioning. Marvellous. Well, I spend nearly a quarter of my waking life worrying about lavatories. So forgive me if I harp on about it. You try sitting for two hours on the bog at a stretch – believe me there are better ways of spending your time. I won't go into the sordid details, but you can imagine the problems as I've got minimal use of my arms and hands so I can't even flush it. That is the least of the problems. I wear an appliance – strapped to my leg. We call it a kipper. 'Cos it looks like one, I suppose. So I don't have much of a problem. But if you ever see a man with his foot in the urinal – he's not gone bonkers – he's draining his kipper....

Now I know what all you little evil minds are thinking. How do they have it away, eh? Isn't that so? Quite apart from the fact that it's too disgusting to think about – I mean physically handicapped people actually wanting sex. Censor that cripple's thoughts – too disgusting. But as you're all interested anyway, I'll tell you. I've done it, since the accident. Not all of us can, it depends, but I can. Bit unpredictable, mind you. Never quite sure what's going on, and talk about *Kama Sutra*. My God – half the time a fork-lift truck would come in handy. But it's possible, always considering a willing partner. Actually many can't work up the necessary steam and that's a bit of a blow. They do say about spinal injuries that they spend half the time on the bog and the other half worrying about being impotent. So it's a full life.

It was in 1972 that this account of an accident was written. Jeff and I were attending Hereward College of Further Education for physically handicapped school-leavers in Coventry. Jeff was a student and I was a lecturer in History. I can remember sitting in one of the corner lounges in the residential blocks talking for hours about what it was like to be disabled, asking questions and taking notes. Jeff's account was particularly fascinating because he remembered all the irrelevant details. He remembered with absolute clarity what his father was wearing, what he looked like when he was so distressed at his son's condition. Jeff even remembered seeing the circling seagulls above him. I later found that this passion for detail was common amongst people who had had accidents. It was also common that at the critical moment they knew something had gone dramatically wrong but were prepared to dismiss that and be upset at trivial things, such as a new pair of trousers ruined.

But this account also triggered off the idea that theatre rather than any other medium was the appropriate one for telling such stories. In a way it was inevitable that theatre would be first in my thoughts, as my own experience and interest had led me in that direction before I, as an able bodied person, ever contemplated working with disabled people. However, there were other reasons. One was the sheer drama of the incident. It is scarcely possible to imagine a more traumatic and dramatic event than diving into the sea one minute and the next being dragged out severely and permanently crippled. The matter-of-fact way in which Jeff related the story made the impact all the greater. Having relived the incident a million times, he was now a little detached from it and he spoke in an objective, unemotional way. In fact my rewriting of it added a passion and bitterness that were certainly lacking in the original conversation.

Another factor in the theatricality of such an event was the sheer chance of it all. It was the moment of fate, the moment when Jeff actually left the ground on his dive, that determined what would happen. As soon as his feet were in the air, it was inevitable that he would break his neck. The moment of fate recurs in all the accident stories I've heard. One girl was hitching home and fell asleep, thus missing the turn-off she wanted. The next car she took was the one that crashed. If she hadn't fallen asleep, if Jeff had looked down into the water for a second before he dived, then neither of them would have ended up in wheelchairs. Not that time, anyway. I think it is Anouilh in *Antigone* who makes his heroine talk about a spring wound up. When it is released, it is inevitable that it will unwind.

It was now that I began to think about how the stories that disabled people had to tell might be developed into some sort of performance.

It might well be argued, and indeed often has been, that the story of a personal traumatic event is private. If somebody chooses to tell me about it in conversation then that is between that person and myself. Any publication or broadcast of the story is an infringement of that confidence. This, of course, may well be so, and is a subject that still troubles the Graeae Theatre Company in the working methods we have adopted. However, in the very early days it was the decisive factor in my desire to present such material as theatre. Never before had disabled people had the chance to talk about their experiences in such a way. Political meetings, discussion groups, awareness classes had provided one sort of forum, but theatre was a totally different one. I believed at the time, and still do, that theatre can present things more dynamically, more excitingly and more memorably than any number of talking heads on TV or than cosy discussion classes. In a phrase, it was the sense of danger in theatre that I found attractive. In exposing an audience to real experiences in a theatrical context there was bound to be some sort of frisson.

The story of what happened next, how the ideas were developed and what the ramifications were is largely the story of this book. Indeed that original script – Jeff's description of his accident – started me off on the road that led to the formation of our full-time theatre company of disabled actors, the Graeae Theatre Company (named after the three old ladies of Greek mythology who shared between them one eye and one tooth). However, I hope the book is more than a catalogue or chronology of what has happened in the intervening years. Inevitably the founding and the development of the company forms an integral part because that is the main experience I have to call on. But that experience sponsors wider debates and discussions, and I hope that many of the issues that attract constant comment after performance now, will get a good airing. So I include chapters that go into much more depth, such as 'Why Theatre?' and 'What Form of Theatre?'

Another purpose of the book is to introduce readers to the working methods adopted by Graeae in the development of its own work and in the use of workshops for both able-bodied and disabled people. In no respect is it an attempt to tell people how plays should be developed or how workshops should be run. It is merely an account of how we have done it. But out of that and out of the case studies I provide, I hope ideas and techniques emerge that can be used and developed by anybody seriously interested in taking drama and theatre as an activity. I have had many inquiries from those interested in working with disabled people in this field, and many are doing tremendous work in such places as hospitals, schools, prisons and day centres. Their techniques and methods will vary enormously. Graeae is only now developing its own techniques and methods: every new rehearsal, every new workshop, provides insight into better ways of doing things next time.

I comment briefly on some of the work that was done in 1981: that year had been designated the International Year of Disabled People, and it was inevitable that writers, theatres and actors should show some interest, as indeed they did. Naturally, some companies – usually those with their own disabled actors – had been working long before 1981 and will be working long after. It is to be hoped that the exposure that 1981 provided for them will generate sufficient impetus to keep them going for a long time yet.

I have included a script from the Graeae Theatre Company. In the section on Graeae's own work I go into some detail on how certain decisions were reached, how improvisations were used, and so on. As this whole section relates specifically to our latest play, *M3 Junction 4*, it seemed only right to include the final script so that the creative process could be seen as near whole as possible. I add that reservation because with Graeae,

scripts are never so sanctified that they cannot be changed,
developed or shortened. As the author of the first of those
scripts I can say this with some authority; it is always a
welcome relief to recognise one's own words amongst
everybody else's.

Finally I offer a brief chapter on what happens next. By the
time this book is published, it – or something entirely different
– will have happened. That is one of the problems of crystal
ball gazing. None the less, I feel it may be helpful to offer a few
comments in the full knowledge that our thinking will progress
and change. In retrospect it will provide a useful index of our
thinking at this particular point.

To go back to *High Dive*, the script that started it all: in fact
Jeff, the true owner of the script, never delivered it. It was
performed by another student at the college, also in a
wheelchair, but as a result of a different accident. In
attempting to make the piece more immediate and real we tried
to recreate the accident using slides, but setting it in the
context of the usual experiences that people have of water,
which are enjoyable:

(*The stage is dark. Suddenly at the back of the stage on a screen a
series of pictures is flashed up. They are pictures of the sea,
rivers, waves crashing, surfing, swimming, boating. Then,
incongruously, of a pair of feet on a diving board. In a series of
slides, the knees tense, the toes flex. The knees straighten. The
toes leave the board.*)

VOICE: Stop! Hold it there! Just exactly there! No, I think
          it's too late. The toes are just leaving. Just above
          the board, by a fraction. It's too late. Can't we
          move it back? It's only a film. (*Pause.*) Oh hell, we
          can't. It's stuck. Well that's not right, can't be
          right. We can't go back, so let's go forward. Come
          on, man! (*Shouts*) Come on! This is the sort of time
          when people start throwing things. Making shapes
          in front of the light. (*Sings*) Why are we waiting?
          Why are we waiting? (*Pause.*) Well, it looks as if

I'll have to take over. Here goes. Captured there. In that photograph are my feet. Yes, my feet. Five toes on each, big toes, little toes, toenails, the lot. And look, just there, on the ankle of the right leg, a scar. You know how I got that? My brother hit me with an axe. Homicidal little swine. (*Laughs.*) Grown up now. Very respectable. Still, that's neither here nor there. But I'm just proving to you that that is my right leg. Not that you'd necessarily recognise anybody by their legs.

Did you like the pictures of the sea and the water? Great, weren't they? Beautiful water. Long, soft silver strips. Have you watched it? Really watched it? Of course you have. There it is. Minuscule drops. Microcosmic oceans each one. Together what vastness, what energy! People just sit and watch it, don't they? Just sit and watch. I've spent hours doing it. Not actually looking for anything – just letting it take over my mind and ebb and flow. Oh, it's smashing, water is. How about those waves? How do those surfers do it? There they are suspended midway up a breaker that's about the size of a house about to fall on them. It breaks.

Thunder and spray everywhere and, miracle of miracles, there's the surfer, tiny, fragile and zinging into the beach like a bat out of hell. (*The frame changes and we see the view that the diver must see. Softer, oilier water off the edge of a pier.*) Hey. What's happened? It's moving again. (*The slide stays.*) No, it's stuck again. What the devil's that? More water. Not quite so nice, is it? Pollution the curse of our age, that's what it is. (*Pause.*) Wait a minute, that water looks strangely familiar – strangely familiar. It's ... where the hell ... it's ... got it. I knew I knew that water. It's just off the edge of a pier and.... (*The slide moves – a picture of feet higher.*) Oh God, look what he's doing. *(Another slide. Slides move quickly now as the body rises in the air, to dive.)*

No, it's not. It can't be. It's me, isn't it? It's me all the time. Stop the film. Stop it. It's me. Those were my feet. My feet. Don't let him. Don't let me. *(Several fast shots of the oily water approaching fast.)* Stop it. Stop. Don't. *(The last slide shows the water virtually at entry point.)*

(Blackout.)

This script was my first attempt to make theatrical a real event. It's important because we have been trying to do just that ever since, with all our productions.

1: Why Theatre?

A natural riposte to the question 'Why Theatre?' would be 'Why not?' One could argue that disabled people have as much right as any other members of society to participate in a performing act. While one would not wish to deny this in principle, the reality for most disabled people was that they would only be accepted on able-bodied terms. That is to say, if they managed to get an entrée to, for example, an amateur theatre group, they could only contribute in a limited number of areas. Disabled people as prompts, or costume makers or scenery painters, were quite often acceptable. As actors they were not. Even the late Michael Flanders, who himself had opened one door by performing the cabaret-style shows *At the Drop of a Hat* with Donald Swann, recommended radio as the most suitable medium. So the very decision to use theatre, although at the time innocent, was in fact flying in the face of most disabled people's experience, as well as being contrary to any competent advice that we could get.

The other factor which could have persuaded us against our intended course of action was the commonly shared experience of performing in and watching shows performed by the disabled. They were usually produced at special schools, as an end-of-term offering, or at special 'disabled' events, and they usually consisted of a lot of bonhomie and group singing, combined with the expectation that the audience would make allowances for the poorness of the performance because all the participants were disabled. We summarised this sort of show as the 'didn't they do well, considering' type. In fact this phrase came to be the goad with which to motivate Graeae performances.

It is necessary to draw some sort of distinction between 'drama' and 'theatre'. As I understand the former, it is involved with the process of creation and can operate at all levels – from playing games like charades, to role playing, to improvisation. Its objective is not performance as such – although that might be part of it – but to explore whatever happens to be the subject. It is a proper educational activity. In fact there are many teachers and indeed organisations that sponsor this sort of work with handicapped people. Theatre, on the other hand, is to do with performance. Although drama may have played a crucial role in the development of the piece being performed, it is hidden to the observer. Performance is staged; it involves a ritual that requires the presence of a – usually – non-participatory, passive audience. It was performance that particularly interested me, and for several reasons, most of which are connected with the fact that the performers are handicapped. Any other reasons are to do with the sort of theatre that I like.

In the first instance, performance gives the performer power. This is true of any performance, given by any person anywhere. The very fact that an audience recognises a performance results in its attention being focused on the performer. To attract attention, it may be necessary to bang a drum or to wear a strange costume. If one walks round Edinburgh at the time of the Festival one can be in no doubt that any number of people are preparing to give or are actually giving performances in the street. And this act of recognition – the passer-by saying 'Ah, that looks interesting, I wonder what they're going to do' – immediately places the observer in the passive role. He or she will watch to see what happens. Maybe later he or she will join in the action, but the action and the observer's involvement have been initiated by the performer.

Now this may all seem rather academic, but for a disabled person it can be nothing short of revolutionary. For it is not generally accepted by society that disabled people are initiators of activities, that they are in charge, or can take command.

In pre-performance talks the most common topic was this

one of power. The company would be reminded that they were in control. They were on the stage. The audience was there to watch them. Only the company knew what happened next.

It has been commented that society expects its crippled members to act crippled. The implication of this is that the bearing of a crippled person, when in the company of a non-crippled person, should be submissive and acquiescent. This view was endorsed by a deaf woman who, in a recent conference, talked about the association between 'faulty ears' and 'faulty person'. She made the point that too often it was thought that because her hearing was faulty, the rest of her was similarly tainted. She ended with the ringing cry that just because she was deaf, she wasn't daft – in fact she was bloody clever.

This blanket view of disability is also illustrated by the title of the well known radio programme, 'Does He Take Sugar?', and by innumerable anecdotes from disabled people. Unfortunately some disabled people actually reinforce this image. They are apathetic. They are lacking in decisiveness. They are submissive and they readily concur with the wishes of the powerful (able-bodied) members of the community. It can become a self-fulfilling prophecy, because society wants it that way.

Paradoxically, society is prepared to eulogise those disabled people that it sees as breaking away from this mould, to the extent that they create folk heroes of them. Douglas Bader is one obvious example. More recently, Police Constable Olds, who became paralysed due to gunshot wounds while trying to apprehend a thief, has had inordinate newspaper and TV coverage. This is not to say that Bader and Olds are not remarkable men. Rather it indicates the lengths that society is prepared to go to create a fictional cardboard cut-out. They both fit the 'wounded hero' stereotype and are treated accordingly. It is almost impossible to clear away the garbage created by the media to get to the real person.

Not so with performance: the very act of controlling the particular medium for a certain time in front of a largely passive, captive crowd, actually does allow for the possibility of clearing away much of the mythology that has been created about disability.

So performance gives power. The very fact of power creates status. In general the status of disabled people in society is low. Recent research on the types of jobs held by disabled people indicates clearly that they hold lower-paid, lower-status jobs, in worse conditions than their able-bodied counterparts (*Unqualified and Underemployed: Handicapped Young People and the Labour Market*, A. Walker, Macmillan). And the number of disabled people who are unemployed is totally out of proportion to their total numbers. In a recent TV programme the one-time Minister for the Disabled, Alf Morris, actually put the figure of disabled people unemployed at 80 per cent in some areas. Jobs give status. Jobs in theatre give a special kind of status. They may not always be regarded as real work, but they give the entry ticket to the most unlikely levels of society. Who, other than an actor, dressed, to say the least, casually, although admittedly in a wheelchair, could expect to be entertained at the United Nations building in Vienna for lunch, and then go on to the British Ambassador's for a quick drink before dinner?

But status is often most obvious in the way people behave towards you. The tendency for most able-bodied people to expect disabled people to be passive and submissive is perhaps even more pronounced in the case of a professional, for example an occupational therapist, whose normal perception of a disabled person is as patient or client. In a recent workshop at a day centre it was most noticeable that the occupational therapist viewed herself as being in the dominant role with her clients, even when the setting was social and not professional. However, her attitude towards members of Graeae, themselves all disabled, who had just taken a workshop, was as to fellow professionals. Having seen a disabled person take charge and initiate action, she could recognise that person as an equal. She obviously did not see her clients in the same light, or even as having that potential. Status breeds confidence and self-respect. It also breeds peer respect.

Performance means responsibility and risk. A performer is responsible to his audience, to his writer, to his directors, for the period of time that he occupies the stage. He is in sole charge. There is nothing the writer or the director can do during the performance. Also, the performer takes the risk of being howled down, abused, misunderstood. He has only himself, his lines and his fellow actors to rely on.

Now both responsibility and risk are relatively rare companions for a disabled person. Very often the environment in which he or she has grown up has been a caring and loving one, full of understanding for the disabled person's deficiencies and very protective against the cruelties of the real world. Parents of disabled children are understandably apprehensive and cautious; schools are concerned about the dangers of failure to the individual. And so it is something of a novelty for a disabled person (the performer) to be put in complete charge of two hours of a group of people's lives (the audience). It is rare for disabled people to be encouraged to take that responsibility in the full knowledge that if they do not succeed and that audience walks out, or expresses condescension or pity, they have failed. So responsibility and risk walk hand in hand, and for the disabled person who takes the risk, takes the responsibility – and succeeds – it is especially gratifying. Until the next performance.

There are other reasons why theatre is such an important medium for disabled people. It allows for enlightenment and education; it is a tool whereby the reality of disability and the realities of people who have disabilities can be introduced, demonstrated and discussed. Plays such as Brian Clark's *Whose Life is it Anyway?* and Tom Klempinski's *Duet for One* both explore individuals in crisis. One is a tetraplegic contemplating suicide, the other a woman with multiple sclerosis. Although both pieces work exceptionally well as theatre, they are, of course, only vicarious experiences, both for the actors and the audience. That is not to denigrate the plays or the performers. They have created a reality for the time that the curtain has been up. At the end they stand up and take their bow. The point is that with a company of disabled actors, they live with their disability after the end of the show. They do not get up out of a wheelchair to take a bow, because they can't.

It used to be a favourite game to discuss what Hamlet had for breakfast on the day he despatched Ophelia to a nunnery. In fact Stoppard's dazzling play *Rosencrantz and Guildenstern are Dead* virtually does that. In other words, there is a fascination with what is taking place in the wings away from the action that is being presented on stage. In one sense the audience knows the answer to that with a company such as Graeae. The blind do not start seeing nor the deaf start hearing once they are off stage. The irony is that when they are on stage, the audience often refuses to accept that a blind actress is in fact blind, or a deaf actress deaf.

The reality of the performers' situation in fact gives validity to the comments made on stage. Just as Jewish jokes or Irish jokes are seen as less racist when the joke-teller happens to be Jewish or Irish, so it is more acceptable for a disabled person to tell a joke about disability than an able-bodied person. But because the public is still uncertain as to its role, there is a greater element of bad taste in the case of Disability jokes. It is generally held that you shouldn't mock the afflicted, and even if it is the afflicted mocking the afflicted, you shouldn't laugh. I am not totally convinced that all audiences would agree with the Monty Python definition of humour, that no matter how tasteless, if it's funny it's all right.

But on the other hand, this uncertainty as to the status of Disability jokes as far as taste is concerned can be used to great advantage. The very fact of uncertainty brings into question other commonly held 'certainties': that, for example, 'the disabled are courageous' or are 'only going to marry other disabled people'.

Here is a sketch that uses the second of these examples. It is entitled *Beauty and the Beast*, and while being a crass rewriting of the fairy story, is also a lampoon of the attitude that expects a disabled person to have a close relationship only with another disabled person.

BEAST:	I've fallen in love.
ALL:	Aaaah!!!!
ACTOR 1:	Isn't that lovely?
ACTOR 2:	Is she able-bodied?
BEAST:	Yes, she is able-bodied.
ACTOR 3:	Sounds like Beauty and the Beast to me.
NARRATOR:	Once upon a time there was a beautiful girl. She was so beautiful that everyone called her Beauty although her real name was Gladys. She lived in a little cottage in the woods with her father who was very poor.
FATHER:	Oh woe. I am very poor. Oh I am. Oh woe. Nothing to eat. Nothing to drink, nothing to wear. Oh dear, oh dear, what shall I do?
BEAUTY:	Do not fear, Papa. I will go and take in washing.
NARRATOR:	So off she set to town. The way led through the dark, dense forest. In the forest there was a castle inhabited by a horrible, twisted, grotesque cripple. In other words, THE BEAST.
BEAST:	Oh I am a beast. Yes I am. All crippled and horrible. Drooling with lust for a lovely fair young maiden who isn't all nasty and crippled. (*Catches sight of* BEAUTY.) Aha, what do I see? Come here you beautiful maiden you, I want you.
BEAUTY:	Oh oh, go away, you dissolute brute you.
BEAST:	But I love you. Can't you love me? I worship the ground you tread on. Can you have no feelings for one who loves so passionately?
BEAUTY:	Well, it's all a bit sudden. Anyway, how can you expect me to love a nasty dissolute misshapen monster like you? I don't love you at all. In fact I find you quite disgusting. Take that horrible face away from me.
NARRATOR:	The Beast was cut to the quick. He went back to his castle dragging the maid with him.

BEAST:	I shan't let you go until you love me.
BEAUTY:	Oh no, oh no. I have to go to town. Let me go, you nasty beast, let me go.
BEAST:	No! You shall love me. You'll learn to. You'll stay here until you do.
NARRATOR:	The Beast did not subject her to nameless abuses (although he thought about it), but wrote letters expressing his undying love. He was distracted with love and poured riches on her. He even wrote poetry.
BEAST:	(*First writing it down before giving it to* BEAUTY.) I love you. My love is true. The sky is blue. (*The maiden throws it away.*)
NARRATOR:	Meanwhile the fair maiden is not having a good time either.
BEAUTY:	How can this foul beast expect me to love him? I mean I'm a reader of *Vogue* and *Country Life* and I'm really rather chic. And he's so yuckee . . . and oh my poor papa. I had a dream that he is ill and worse. What am I to do? If only I could escape with some of the riches that foul drooling beast has given me. I could get to town and sell them for money and get a doctor and make him better.
NARRATOR:	As she planned, the Beast made a final effort to win the affections of the maiden with some more ghastly poetry.
BEAST:	(*Presenting poem and flower to* BEAUTY.) Roses are red. Violets are blue. Accept this flower or (*raspberry*) to you!
BEAUTY:	Oh well, it can't do any harm. (*The* BEAST *is overjoyed.*) But now here is my chance. The servant has left the door open. I will steal away

and sell the Beast's treasure.

NARRATOR: To cut a long story short, that is exactly what she did. She went to town, sold the treasure, got a doctor, took him to her poor old dad, made him better, and they all started living it up on the money they had left. Beauty forgot all about the Beast until, one day, she saw that her flower had gone all droopy.

BEAUTY: Oh look. It's gone all droopy. I wonder what has happened to the poor old Beast. He wasn't a bad guy really.

NARRATOR: Then as was her wont, Beauty had a dream. In it she saw the Beast pining away with love.

BEAST: Oh pine, pine!

BEAUTY: The poor old Beast. Oh woe, what have I done? There is true love even if I did not appreciate it at the time. Now didn't I once read about a beautiful maiden who fell in love with a horrible Beast? And didn't she kiss him? And didn't he turn into a handsome prince? Handsome prince. Big castle. Lots of money. Oh I must go and help him. Goodbye, papa.

NARRATOR: So she rushed back to the castle and there was the Beast lying prostrate beneath the bush which had the flowers one of which he had given to Beauty.

BEAUTY: Oh, my poor Beast. Here I come, do not fear, Beauty is here.

NARRATOR: And now the crucial bit. Would the Beast turn into a prince when she kissed him? Beauty, taking her courage in her hand, puckered her lips and gave him a smacker. Nothing happened.

BEAUTY: You are not a prince.

BEAST: I've got everything but the looks. And who needs looks when you're as nice as I am?

BEAUTY: In the story even the frog turned into a prince when the princess kissed it.

BEAST:	Do you think I'd love anybody dumb enough to go round kissing frogs?
BEAUTY:	I suppose not.
BEAST:	Of course not. So I am who I am. If you don't like it there's nothing I can do about it.
BEAUTY:	I wouldn't have known what to say to a prince anyhow. (*They embrace.*)
NARRATOR:	Of course Papa was delighted.
FATHER:	My child. Her life ruined by marrying a social outcast. Oh woe. What shall I do? Poor me.
BEAST:	I shall be a dutiful son-in-law. I'll even give you a job as a butler in the castle, so you're no longer poor. Now wrap up.
NARRATOR:	So that was that and for once Beauty and the Beast got on fine. And the better you knew them the harder it was to tell who was Beauty and who was the Beast.

This sketch, from the 1981 version of *Sideshow*, always worked remarkably well, largely because the Beast, played originally by Nabil Shaban, was so endearing that nobody actually wanted him to turn into a sugar-sweet, handsome prince. The scene was further complicated by the fact that the actress playing Beauty was invariably handicapped. The part has been played variously by a girl in a wheelchair, a blind girl, a deaf girl, and finally a partially sighted boy. Never has a member of the audience commented after a show that the point being made by the sketch was undermined by the casting of the principal players. This indicates to me that the audience has in fact accepted the premise laid down at the start: that Beauty will be able-bodied and the Beast will not.

It is always hard to assess the impact of a show on an audience, let alone a small section of the show such as this sketch. All one can say is that the two people who have played the part of the Beast, Bob Trotter in the USA and Nabil Shaban everywhere else, were not short of able-bodied female admirers after the show. Maybe this has more to do with their own personal charm than any message in the play. Perhaps the latter complemented the former.

Sideshow deliberately set out to enlighten attitudes, either by lampooning stereotypes as in *Beauty and the Beast* or by confronting an audience with a direct challenge as in this piece of verse:

> The world is so twee and nice
> It's full of candy and spice
> We get pats on the head
> For being good
>
> It's full of people who care
> Who are kind-hearted and fair
> They feed us with
> Saccharine food
>
> We smile in sweet gratitude
> And act as all cripples should
> Like marzipan figures
> On a cake
>
> We're filled with cream and meringue
> And we're sweet to the tongue
> We're gaudy and gay
> For your sake
>
> Do we have to pretend
> That this in the end
> Is all that
> We're living for
>
> To entertain throngs
> With laughter and songs
> Is this an inescapable
> Law
>
> Is each man in his place
> And does impairment debase
> So that we are put
> Where we belong

> For a sweet tooth decays
> And the roles that we play
> Have words
> That don't go in songs
>
> And the ache in my mind
> Rots my soul from inside
> And the taste in my mouth
> Makes me spit
>
> Let me be what I am
> I don't give a damn
> It's me that I've got
> And that's it.

The bitterness with which the final stanzas were delivered was a deliberate shock tactic. Audiences were often totally silent at the end of the scene, although disabled members sometimes indicated their approval and identification with the sentiment expressed.

So theatre can aim at enlightenment and education. It can give information as well as attempt to alter attitudes. Here is an example from a very early play, developed at Hereward College in Coventry mentioned in the Introduction and entitled *Never Mind, You'll Soon Get Better*. It was the result of discussions with two students both of whom had spina bifida, and who wanted the opportunity to tell an audience about it. This they proceeded to do in cheery, matter-of-fact tones:

LINDA: I have the second most popular disability. Spina bifida.

ALL: Spina what?

LINDA: Spina bifida. Don't you ignorant people know anything? First slide please. (*Slide showing a spine that has spina bifida.*) What this means is that I was born with a spine that was laid open, exposing the spinal cord. All very grisly. And in fact up to about ten years ago the likelihood of people surviving was not good at all. But now, what with medical know-how and what not, some 50 per cent are surviving. Rising in considerable popularity we are, although they're not sure exactly how many of us there are. Back to the information. When you're born with spina bifida, then you usually have an operation to cover over the spine – giving some a sort of hump on the back.

PHILIP: But by then it usually means you're paralysed from the waist down like me. Some 60 per cent of spina bifida are and the remainder usually have some sort of lower limb defect. This also means that 49 per cent are incontinent. There is also a strange thing that can happen with spina bifida and that is hydrocephalus or big-headedness like me. Great swollen bonces. If it goes on too long, then I'm afraid you've had it. But again the doctors have got something for that. They drain the fluid round the brain, that is causing the swollen head – into the heart. If anybody's feeling ill, there are brown paper bags under the seats. Anyway it's all quite simple. I'm one of the 25 per cent who need aids to walk. These (*waves crutches*).

LINDA: I'm one of the 15 per cent chairbound.

PHILIP: Quite. (*To audience*) Any questions? Any questions?

This technique was used frequently in another show which grew out of *Never Mind, You'll Soon Get Better* and was entitled *Ready Salted Crips*. In this next example a series of facts was used to illustrate the size of the population affected by some form of disability. The comparisons are quite startling and reflect critically on the weight given by the media to respective disadvantaged groups. The two approaches of assaulting entrenched attitudes with satire and using facts to sustain an argument are used here.

ACTOR   (*Dressed as World War II airman crosses centre stage with display board for illustrations.*) Briefing time again, chaps, and here is your favourite World War II escapee.

Now if you take all the miners and all the railwaymen and finally all the police, you have a grand figure of 760,000 people. And we all know what happens if one or all of them go on strike. Well, it may fascinate you to know that that is the same number of handicapped people working at this moment. Just imagine if they all went on strike.

Further, to blind you with meaningless figures, there are some 36,000 people in prison. Multiply that by eight and you get 288,000. That number is slightly less than the number of people under retirement age who cannot work because of their disability. Eight times the prison population deprived of earning a living with no disability pension to help them.

Dear oh dear, gloom and despondency everywhere. Too bloody miserable for words.

A sketch such as *Beauty and the Beast* is aimed at all the audience. But at times we wanted to be more specific, to comment on a particular section of the audience. One obvious target for parody is the medical profession. Disabled people, more than most, have their fill of hospitals, doctors, surgeons, therapists and nurses; their views, fairly or unfairly, can be seen as pretty cynical. Here is a sketch devised in the USA. It seems to have taken parody to the limits of absurdity, and yet it is absolutely accurate, except that the surgeons come over as mechanics rather than medical practitioners. The operations described did take place. The final one, on the head, really happened, and the results were just as described by the actor.

RING MASTER:	Our next act is the Medical Profession and their streamlined 1976 bicentennial model of that old standard prototype, the Congenitally Handicapped Person.
ACTRESS with CP:	CP is Cerebral Palsy. (*Comes forward centre stage.*) I was born a perfectly ordinary, normal CP. There was no end of things I couldn't do. I couldn't walk, use my hands properly or even talk very well. I could understand most of what went on around me, but I couldn't do much about it.
DOCTOR:	(*As car mechanic.*) Can't have this. Old-fashioned model. (*All the while the doctor is examining with screw driver, banging arms and legs, etc.*) Broken down. Not working properly. Terrible state of repair. Mobility no good. Trouble with the traction rods. The upper flange sprocket gasket head of the left knee doesn't look too good either. Have to take it into the garage.
2nd DOCTOR:	Dear me, what bad shape that old wreck is in. Suspension, electrics, ignition, transmission, it's all in need of work.
Both DOCTORS:	What you need is a complete overhaul.
ACTRESS with CP:	And so I started to have operations.
1st DOCTOR:	Right, suspension first.
ACTRESS with CP:	They operated on my legs. (*All through this the doctors are miming operations with large spanners, hammers etc.*)
2nd DOCTOR:	Don't like the look of those engine bearings.
ACTRESS with CP:	Then it was my hips. And so on. Eleven in all. (*Doctors, after much play, finish their work.*)

1st DOCTOR:	Right, let's have a look at it now. Hmm. Get up. (*Actor attempts to. After a struggle she fails.*)
2nd DOCTOR:	It's still not right, you know.
1st DOCTOR:	We're just going to have to have a look at that motor. The problem must originate there.
2nd DOCTOR:	Yes, these CPs aren't easy, are they?
1st DOCTOR:	Now if we . . . (*They go into a huddle to discuss what they should do.*)
ACTRESS with CP:	So they started on my last operation. On my head.
2nd DOCTOR:	You see, it's the electrics. So we'll implant two electrodes on the brain. (*Using the other doctor as a model the 2nd doctor puts headphones round the head. She holds the lead and also a lead coming from a large battery.*) Like this, see. Under the skin. And these are stimulated by a battery. We have wires coming down inside the neck to join about here. (*Indicates.*) And the wires coming from the battery. And when they join we should get some results. (*With much exaggerated drama the doctor joins the two leads. The other doctor goes into a frenzy — steam from his ears, etc. They both look disconcerted.*) Well, I'm sure it will work OK.
ACTRESS with CP:	And so that is what they did. Here is my battery. And look at the difference. You can understand what I say. I can use my left hand for carrying things. It really is quite remarkable. (*To the two doctors*) Well, what do you think?

2nd DOCTOR:	It's still not perfect, but still we're getting somewhere, aren't we?
ACTRESS with CP:	Now come on, you guys. Haven't you done enough? I think I'll just stick as I am.
1st DOCTOR:	Oh come on, it was just getting fun. I mean we could have a go at a transplant of some sort. It's all progress you know. You realise that you've got more hardware in you than an Everest and Jennings factory?
2nd DOCTOR:	Well, don't worry (*this to other doctor*). We are sure to find another broken-down model to play with. (*To audience*) You just wait until you see our 1986 model. Just watch out, Bionic Woman.

This scene leads me to the last part of the answer to the question, 'Why theatre?' As I have said, bizarre as it may seem, the operation on the head there described is accurate in every detail. The actress at that time had, and still has as far as I know, a battery which was connected by wires to electrodes implanted on her brain. The context in which she explains this is obviously theatrical and yet, I would argue, not absurdly unfair on the medical profession.

All the scenes detailed above, however crude, cruel or one-sided, have grown out of the personal experience of the actor or indeed of all the company. Marion Saunders, for instance, a founder member of Graeae, recounts how a faith healer attempted to make her walk in spite of her being in a wheelchair, as a result of muscular dystrophy.

Increasingly, we found that personal experience rather than objective fact provided our most theatrical and riveting material. On the one hand an anecdote could be the springboard for a sketch such as that on the 1976 congenitally handicapped person, quoted above. On the other, it could be a reconstruction of a real event. This is exactly the case with the seminal script *High Dive*, quoted in the Introduction. The

reality of this theatre of personal experience has immense
theatrical strength. In every production there has been a re-
telling of an accident: here is the description of Judy's accident
which was performed as part of *Ready Salted Crips*:

ANNOUNCER:	(*Comes forward with map.*) On July 25th, 1969, two girls set out to hitch-hike from Manchester to Lincoln. They had been to an all-night party. Both girls were dressed in jeans and a jersey. It was raining in Manchester.
JUDY:	I was wearing shoes that had a hole in them. My feet were getting wet.
ANNOUNCER:	To get to Lincoln one travels from Stockport along the A6 to Chapel-en-le-Frith and turns off to Sheffield along the A625. Through Sheffield you take the A57 to Lincoln. A distance of ninety odd miles in all. The first vehicle to pick them up was a lorry. The time was about 11.00 a.m. Both the girls were very tired and didn't realise that instead of turning off at the A625, the lorry was continuing down the A6 to Derby. The alternative route to Lincoln was to turn off just before Belper and try and get a lift along the A610 to Nottingham, and then take the A612 and the A46 back to Lincoln. With this in mind, they got off the lorry at the junction with the A610. After a wait, they got a lift to Nottingham.
JUDY:	It was a lovely and sunny going through Nottingham.
ANNOUNCER:	It took a couple of lifts and a bus journey to get through Nottingham. They managed to get a lift a little way along the A612 before being dropped about here. Here they waited and waited.

JUDY:	At last a navy blue 1100 pulled up. There were three blokes inside.
BLOKE:	Where are you going?
JUDY:	Lincoln. You going there?
BLOKE:	No, we're going to Newark but we can drop you off.
JUDY:	Thanks a lot.
ANNOUNCER:	The girls got in the back of the car. The time was about half past three. Both girls were tired and they dozed. To get to Lincoln, you have to make a left-hand turn on to the A46; it's built up and there is quite a drop down an embankment. The turn is sharp.
BLOKE:	Hey, where do you turn off?
JUDY:	(*Wakening.*) Here! That's it. Just here. *Squeal of brakes and skid. The car goes down the embankment and crashes. There is silence.*)
ANNOUNCER:	The time is three minutes to four. The sky is overcast, but it is not raining. Four of the occupants of the car are thrown clear. The fifth is the girl in the middle at the back. She is thrown forward and hits her head on the ashtray on the floor. Her face and head are covered in blood. The wound will require fifty-six stitches. It is not at first appreciated that she has also broken her neck. (*Noise of ambulance, etc.*)
JUDY:	I don't remember it at all. The crash. I remember the stitches and voices.
NURSE 1:	You all right dear?
JUDY:	And my uncle and aunt coming. They were so far away. I could see their faces high above me and their voices down a tunnel.
(*Recorded.*)	Hello, Judy dear. How are you?

(*Recorded.*)	Hello, Judy dear. How are you?
JUDY:	I'm hungry. Can I have something to eat?
NURSE 1:	We'll have to wait until the doctor sees you first, dear.
JUDY:	Have my mum and dad been? I'm hungry and thirsty.
NURSE 2:	I'm sorry, dear, the doctor's gone. You'll have to wait until tomorrow.
JUDY:	Nurse, can you straighten my legs? They're all folded up.
NURSE 3:	You're in bed dear. You're lying on your back and your legs are on the bed.
JUDY:	No. They're folded up. I can feel them. Can you put them down, please? I'm thirsty.
	(*Pause.*)
	They shaved my head and hung weights from it. They give you a local anaesthetic to bore holes to hang the weights from. The man said he wouldn't hurt me. He only hurt me once. A little old lady gave me some flowers. Roses. Red ones. I'm thirsty. I was always thirsty. And hungry. I hadn't eaten since before the crash. That was about three days ago.
ANNOUNCER:	Judy had been taken to a small local hospital in Newark. After a few days there, she was transferred to Mansfield.
JUDY:	I still had the feeling that they didn't really know what to do with me.
DOCTOR 1:	It looks like a lesion between the fifth and sixth. What does the X-ray show, Bob?
DOCTOR 2:	Well, here we are. Yes, you can see it there.
JUDY:	And doctors gathered in little groups and talked about me. But they never told me anything and I couldn't understand the bits of conversation I could hear. It never

	struck me what was wrong. I never thought about it.
DOCTOR HARDY:	Hello there. Are they feeding you?
JUDY:	That's my specialist, Dr Hardy. As soon as he came I knew it was going to be all right. He sounded so confident. Well, I haven't had much to eat and I am hungry.
DOCTOR HARDY:	Well, we'll soon put that right. And I think, young lady, you'll be coming up to Lodge Moor so that we can have a proper look at you.
ANNOUNCER:	On August 1st Judy was transferred to Lodge Moor, Sheffield, a spinal injury unit.
JUDY:	Lodge Moor was a lot different. I'd become accustomed to people rushing about looking after me. But now, I was just one amongst a whole lot, all with spinal injuries. Next to me was a girl called Janet. She was a spina bifida. I'd never met anyone with spina bifida. It was fascinating. But then there were visitors. My parents lived quite near and they'd come and visit. We'd nothing to say and I'd pretend to be asleep. Oh God, here they come . . . .
	(*She feigns sleep*.)
FATHER:	Hello, dear.
MOTHER:	I think she's asleep.
FATHER:	Perhaps we'd better come back.
MOTHER:	No, we'll wait. It'll soon be tea-time and I'm sure she'll be woken for that.
	(*Pause*.)
NURSE 3:	What's happened to Judy, then? She was awake just a minute ago. Come on, Judy, wake up. It's your mother and father.
JUDY:	What? Oh Yes. Hello Mum, Dad.
MOTHER:	Hello, love, how are you?

JUDY: Oh, not so bad.

FATHER: That's it. Soon have you up and about again.

JUDY: Yes.

MOTHER: Had your Aunt and Uncle round over the weekend. They were asking after you. I'll tell them you're feeling better.

JUDY: Yes.

FATHER: We'll soon be having you home. The Doctor said you may well be home for Christmas. That'll be nice, won't it? (*Exeunt.*)

JUDY: It was always like that, but they always came. Duty, I suppose, and a sort of guilt that wouldn't let them admit that I was crippled. They had to show I was still their child, no matter what. It was the proper thing to do, but I can't say it helped me very much. And I don't think it helped them either.

PHYSIO: Hello, Judy. Let's see how these muscles are working, shall we?

JUDY: This is my physiotherapist. She's ever so nice.

PHYSIO: Now let me see. Press against this with your hand. Good. You can see a bit coming back there. Now the other. That's right.

JUDY: Will my arms ever be right?

PHYSIO: It's hard to say. They've certainly improved just in the last week. You must feel that.

JUDY: Last night I was determined to get my hands from under the bedclothes. I worked and worked and kept needling myself. And I did it. Both of them.

PHYSIO: That's great. I told you something was coming back.

JUDY:	It took an hour, but I did it.
PHYSIO:	Now the legs. Can you feel this? *(She sticks a pin into* JUDY's *toe.)*
JUDY:	I think I can.
PHYSIO:	That's a good sign too. To be able to feel something. Let's try a bit higher up. Feel that?
JUDY:	No.
PHYSIO:	Or there?
JUDY:	No.
PHYSIO:	Well, it often happens. Sensation can be very patchy.
JUDY:	What about my legs?
PHYSIO:	How do you mean?
JUDY:	Well, will they improve?
PHYSIO:	The fact that you can feel something is good. But it's very slow and only little bits come back. You get used to that very quickly and make adaptations. You'll have to get used to making yourself do things that are very hard at first. Even wheeling yourself in a wheelchair will be very difficult. But you must keep working at it. I mean, you've already started with your hands. You've just got to keep plugging away.
JUDY:	I find it difficult with my fingers. I can't grip anything.
PHYSIO:	That may not come back completely. You've got a very high lesion. A break right up here. *(Indicates.)* But the more you work at it the more quickly you'll improve.
JUDY:	Well, I'm certainly going to have a story to tell when I get back to school.
PHYSIO:	Judy . . .
JUDY:	Yes.
PHYSIO:	I don't think you'll be going back to your

	old school. I don't think they'll be able to cope with you in a wheelchair – upstairs and everything.
JUDY:	Oh.
PHYSIO:	You'll still be able to get an education, but you're going to have to change schools. Well that's enough for today. See you tomorrow. Bye.
JUDY:	Bye. (*Pause.*) I went out for the first time a bit later. Janet pushed me. You know, the girl in the next bed. She was in a chair too. She let go at the top of an incline and I just went. I couldn't stop. I fell out at the bottom. And the Doctor said, 'I don't mind you throwing yourself about in a month or two's time, but just a couple of weeks after the accident is not a good idea.' I read a lot. Had a special machine for turning the pages. What was it – *War of the Worlds*, what else . . . And the vicar used to call and bring a choir with him to cheer us all up. *Enter* VICAR.)
VICAR:	Ah, good morning, Judy. How are you today?
JUDY:	All right, thank you.
VICAR:	Now, how can I help you?
JUDY:	Well, Vicar, can you explain why God allowed me to break my neck?
VICAR:	Well, Judy, that's a very difficult question to answer. And I can't give you an adequate one at all. All I can say is that God moves in a mysterious way.
JUDY:	Bloody mysterious.
VICAR:	Quite so. Now how about a song from our choir here. Are we ready? Hymn no. 243. And . . .
CHOIR:	(*Sing*) Stand up, stand up for Jesus, You

soldiers of the cross.

JUDY: The poor Vicar didn't really have much of a chance, did he?

ANNOUNCER: On Christmas Day, Judy was allowed to go home.

JUDY: The car seemed to be going ever so fast.
(*All crowd round.* 'Hello, Judy, hello, Happy Christmas, etc.')

FATHER: Here are your presents.

AUNT: That one's from me.

VOICES: Go on, open it up.

JUDY: I wonder what's in it . . .
(*There is a terrible pause as* JUDY *tries to open the present. Everybody is embarrassed and eventually* JUDY *gives up.*)
I can't undo it.

FATHER: Damn that bloody car driver. If I could get my hands on him I'd kill him.

The tension that scene generated was at times unbearable, especially when Judy was unable to open her present. It seemed an eternity as she struggled with the wrapping. But even such a traumatic event could be laced with humour. The anecdote of the vicar conducting the hymn entitled 'Stand up, stand up for Jesus' in a spinal injury ward is actually true.

This scene speaks volumes about the relationship of one young person with her parents and peers, and it doesn't seem so different from the experience of young people who have not broken their necks.

A more recent production presented a particular challenge because the person talking about his accident had no real memory of it. Will had had quite severe brain damage as a result of being hit by a car. He had been in a coma for three months, and his memory was severely affected as a result. This meant that not only was his memory of the accident extremely hazy, but he couldn't remember his lines on stage. I felt, though, that it was important to portray his accident on stage because the accident was important to Will. The problem was how to do this without placing Will in the impossible position of causing a breakdown of the scene at every performance. It was resolved by first setting up an improvisation whereby all the company sat round and asked him questions about the accident, how he felt and so on. We then sifted those questions down to about ten or a dozen. I directed the company to ask them at every performance, and I asked Will to answer them. In this way he didn't need to learn lines. This improvisation in performance continued over some forty or fifty shows. The results were often staggering. I remember on one occasion, when he was asked the standard question, 'You were once able-bodied, you are now handicapped, how do you feel?', Will replied, 'Useless. I feel useless.' He had never said that before. As the company on stage recognised the total honesty of the response, the effect was electric. This communicated itself to the audience, who were also aware that something special had occurred. The amusing sequel to this is that when I complimented Will on that superbly effective answer he denied he had ever said such a thing and continued denying it for the next couple of weeks.

This reaching into people's experiences was and is the standard Graeae approach. I shall explain in the next chapter why this approach was chosen in preference to the other alternatives that presented themselves. The culmination, to date, of this technique is the play *3D* which the company first performed at the Edinburgh Festival in 1981. This too began with the assumption that disabled people have stories to tell. But this time we settled for a documentary type of approach and asked the five actors to talk about their lives.

For example, Yvonne (who was born with legs and arms foreshortened as a result of thalidomide):

I had to be assessed and examined by two doctors. They had to have two so that they could agree with each other. And they used to send forms for my mum to fill in with questions like, 'How many bones has she got in her left hand?' Well, I mean to say, how many bones have you got in your left hand? You don't know, do you? Even if you have a quick fiddle, you won't get it right. Well, my mum, she used to guess and they'd say, 'That's one fewer than last year – strange!' They never asked me – not that it would have done much good, as I didn't know either.

Or Nabil (who was born with osteogenesis imperfecta – brittle bones):

I've broken bones so often I've lost count. When I was small – I could pull off a sock and break a toe. Don't think it'll happen now. Hope not. Here goes (*pulls off sock*). Don't think so, though that one looks a little ropey. You'd think you'd get used to breaking things, wouldn't you? Wouldn't hurt so much after you'd done it a dozen times? Well, I can assure you it bloody well does. Another thing is, when you break a leg, everybody makes a fuss, signs your plaster cast, looks after you and so on. With me it's so normal, nobody bothers to make a fuss.

Personal stories are never objective, but they do stir memories in everybody's mind.

Here is Yvonne again, remembering how she felt when she reached adolescence:

When I was a kid it was an adventure. I could roll around like one of those wobbly dolls. Even wearing artificial legs was an adventure at first. People used to say encouraging things. Often men used to congratulate me and tell me what a good job I was doing. I liked it. Then one day, I noticed what other girls were wearing. They were so pretty, with lovely legs. And they would wear all sorts of different shoes. I envied them and I really hated what I was. I wanted cosmetic legs that looked right. The colour was always too pink. I wanted them to look real. But they made my bum look bigger. I was like a ball on stilts.

Now everyone has adolescent memories of inadequacy and

embarrassment. Yvonne has them too, and yet they are more pronounced and more intense, because her differences are real and measurable. And for an audience they are recognisable as part of the same spectrum of tensions, ambitions and failures that was their own adolescence.

There are also anecdotes that have nothing to do with disability at all. Some are hilarious, like Jag's description of his first pair of underpants:

> My father took me to hospital in this country for the first time. In India I only used to wear pyjama-type things of cloth round my middle. I'd never worn underpants and my dad thought it important that I should look right, so he bought me a pair. A white pair. Now underpants have a little slit in the front. I didn't know this. And I didn't know what it was for. Then I worked it out – it was so I could hang my willy out. So that's what I did. I put the underpants on carefully and put my willy through the slit. I used to walk around with just my underpants on and my willy (*gesture*). I was very proud of myself. When I went to the toilet, I pushed my willy back in and pulled my pants down to pee.

Or Elane's tragic but terribly familiar story of her father's death:

> I'd gone to college and a month before my part 1 exams I learnt that my father was seriously ill with cancer. There were times when I felt he was dying and so in the middle of trying to revise, I'd burst into tears. I couldn't really talk to anyone about it. I was just another neurotic student with a problem, so I went to see an old friend of his and stayed there four days. It was really strange. I don't know why I did it. I went with my father to the doctor's and was called into the surgery after he had been examined. The doctor told me. How long? A matter of weeks. It really hit me – unbelievable, and yet I totally believed it. My mother wouldn't tell him. The next appointment at the doctor's, I wheeled him in. For the next two weeks the three of us were

together. I'm an only child. He was in the living-room downstairs. They called me at 5.30 one morning. I started to shake him. I had to get through to him. I was the only one who could communicate with him. I knew that. He said he had seen someone in the garden who was waiting for him. He wanted to go to the temple. Get his dressing-gown. Could I come too? Yes I could. It was a temple in Cheltenham. He put his arms around me and he wouldn't let go. Then my mother and I were cleaning windows, arguing. He turned to his sister and said, 'They'll never change.' There were about ten in the lounge, sitting round, and my mother told me to come over. I held his hand. I was very confused. I didn't know whether he was dead or not. I helped lay him out. I couldn't bear the thought of other people doing it. I had to look after him. He was my father and it was a love and an honour. People kept trying to get me out of the room. But I wanted to say goodbye in my own time. I just wanted a bit of time and nobody could understand.

The fact that Jag is cerebrally palsied and Elane blind is totally irrelevant to the stories they relate.

The realisation has grown that theatre is a marvellous medium for disabled people to tell their stories or state their case. It is immediate, real and powerful. I have outlined the main reasons why we have become increasingly convinced that theatre is an essential method of expressing our views. But the way that we have chosen is by no means the only one, nor is it the most obvious. There are other options, other ways of using theatre, which I will now discuss.

2: What Form of Theatre?

It would be wrong to suggest that the form of theatre that was eventually arrived at by the Graeae company represents a definitive position or that alternatives were not, and are not, hotly debated. The discussion turns on how disability is represented on stage and how it is perceived by the audience. Back in 1972 in the first paper that I wrote on the use of theatre for disabled people, the emphasis was strongly on the need to see physical handicap as the common factor in the company, but, if presented in the right way, as a trivial factor.

Students should develop an interpretation of drama that would be acceptable in its own right as a piece of theatre to be viewed and criticised by the general public. Improvised situations in plays could be taken and seen in the light of an audience unused to and slightly repelled by the sight of the physically handicapped. The aim would be to present a play so that the physically handicapped factor is seen as a common denominator to be ignored rather than to be patronised. This would limit the type of play chosen and its interpretation. It would be hard to envisage physically handicapped students doing a situation comedy in realistic staging and getting away with it, but plays that are more symbolic, or plays of absurdity, or surreality or even cruelty could be staged and be perfectly acceptable as theatrical events in their own right.

This common denominator approach follows the example of, say, a black theatre company who, wanting to play *Hamlet*, would not necessarily expect an audience to view the production as a statement of 'blackness' but as just another production of *Hamlet*. This, of course, presupposes that such a theatre company would want to produce a 'non-black' *Hamlet*.

This particular common denominator argument can be seen as naive as it assumes that any minority group who band together to produce shows, do so without any wish to make a statement about their belonging to that group. It is in fact virtually inconceivable that a black group would want to present any play that did not have some reference to black culture, black experience or black aspirations. This is equally true of other minority groups who have put energy into creating theatre – for example, women's groups or gay groups whose very existence is a political statement.

Similarly, disabled people do form a minority group and they do have political ambitions. And yet disability is not so easily and readily identifiable. It has no ethnic, class or cultural roots. It is part of all sections of society and yet it is seen as apart; indeed society looks upon a disability as an inability. As I said in my Introduction disability has a negative image; it is not easy to reverse it to one that is positive and assertive.

Disabled people are usually put in associations with each other, rather than finding a natural affinity. Any such group coming together for theatre may have as their common denominator the wish to act, rather than to make a political statement. Political consciousness about disability amongst disabled people is notoriously low; disability gives no sense of pride or of belonging, and many prefer not to be labelled in that way.

So there was a strong argument right from the start that productions should aim at the normal range in the theatre repertoire. And yet how could they? Not only was there the obvious fact of some actors being in wheelchairs and others on crutches, but if one broadened the category of people eligible to work in this type of theatre to include blind and deaf actors, there was no obvious common denominator amongst handicaps.

Some theatre companies have avoided this problem by

sticking to one disability group. One such is the Theatre of the Deaf which in its newest form is the Interim Theatre Company. Not only does this company have the common denominator of a common handicap, it also has the common denominator of an alternative language in the form of sign and mime. A sort of house style is immediately apparent. Within the confines of that style there are a host of possibilities. Recently, Interim mounted a production of *Equus* at the Young Vic. The fact that the majority of the cast was deaf actually forced them to find a style that could solve technically any communication problems. The overall effect could still be theatrically successful, and indeed could be seen as a novel reading of the play. Thus the play was not about deafness at all: it was simply that deaf people had chosen to do it and to communicate its theme using a specific style.

The Venturers Club, which is a theatre for blind people, actually goes one step further. It presents shows without any acknowledgement that the players are blind. The actors open themselves to a field that is limitless, and would argue that any play is possible because their only problem is technical. That is to say, the range of experience explored in any play is within their scope as actors, but they have to find appropriate ways of moving about on stage and getting on and off without walking into the set or each other, or falling off. Each move has to be carefully planned and measured, so the whole production hinges on an elaborate choreography.

Yet another company, the Theatre of the Disabled, solved the problem by putting all four performers in wheelchairs, although in fact only two of them ordinarily used them.

So how did we cope theatrically with the problems presented by different handicaps – some visible, others not? Very early on the decision was made not to deny a handicap. If it was there, then we shouldn't pretend otherwise. We had presented ourselves with the task of turning the myth that disability was synonymous with inability into the view that disability had to be used. It was to be a positive force, a complement to the characterisation, and not a detraction.

Having established this point, it was important to review the range of plays that could be presented using disability in this way. As I have said, the likelihood of doing a realistic piece was tinged with absurdity. The vision of an actor on crutches bursting through the French windows and crying, 'Anyone for tennis?' was ridiculous, but with a little careful thought there did seem to be some plays that could be viewed as suitable.

We saw the exploration of the theme of disability as a temporary, if necessary, phase. Everybody, including myself, actually wanted to get away from disability: the final proof of whether people with disabilities could actually contribute to theatre, and perform a valid piece, would be to test them out using a conventionally scripted play. This motivation is still present in the company, and outsiders are still commonly heard to reflect that although they found the piece interesting they would like to know when we are 'going to take on a real script'.

The very first 'real' script that we attempted (in 1973) was an adaptation of *Everyman*, the traditional medieval morality play. It was to be full of symbolism and ritual and would use the actors' disabilities deliberately as part of the characterisation. Perhaps this was most successfully demonstrated in the playing of the character, Death. The actor concerned was confined to an electric wheelchair. We played up the sound of the electric motor by letting him circle the stage a couple of times at the start. We also made use of the relatively strange shape of a man in a cumbersome wheelchair by covering both in a black shroud. We hoped that this would convey a threatening image. For those in the know, it was very hard not to view this strange sight as a young man in an electric wheelchair covered in a black cloth. In other words, the success of such a use of disability is questionable. In this instance it was probably a disadvantage that all the company were disabled, as it was fairly obvious what we were attempting to do. In an able-bodied company, a misshapen and grotesque Death might have been far more effective. Other characters were encouraged to a lesser degree to use their visible disabilities as part of the character. An old soldier did not use the fact of his being on crutches as an indication of injury sustained in the execution of duty, but rather as a part of his uniform: his crutches were deliberately painted to match the military stripe in his trousers. The character of Confession was played by a severely disabled student who had cerebral palsy. This not only confined him to a wheelchair, but also affected his speech, so that at times it was unintelligible. He was dressed in sackcloth as a sort of hermit, and the whole effect, although not deliberately so, was hysterically funny. Confession came over as irritable and disreputable; his arms and legs flew everywhere, speech of a sort came out in great gobbets of spit, and Everyman backed away in some distaste. The fact that the character was given lines such as 'Penitence, that's what you need, penitence. Sackcloth and ashes. Scourge that evil flesh. Scourge and do penance, you miserable sinner. Scourge! Scourge! Scourge!' actually helped. Although it was by no means clear what Confession was saying, his intentions were pretty clear and Everyman could not have been reassured by his attitude.

This scene of the play worked well probably because the humour in it was obvious. But at the time, I think, we were a little disillusioned, as we felt the experiment to prove that disabled people could provide meaningful drama had rather failed.

The next script that we attempted was *Schoolplay* by Donald Howarth. This is a very short piece consisting of a classroom of pupils and a teacher. Everybody has a script, and the play is virtually static and more a reading than a performance. All the pupils are numbered one to however many are present. All are asked to respond to their number being called out. One does not do so, and all the interaction is triggered by this act of non-cooperation. Howarth considered that the piece could and should be used in an ordinary classroom setting. Disability plays no part in the proceedings, and anyway there was no discernible way of using it. The performance was confined to an in-house audience of fellow students, staff, families and friends, and in that context the common denominator theory could hold up.

The show that eventually emerged as *Sideshow* was evolving at the same time as these experiments in other, conventional, kinds of theatre. So there was no firm commitment to one style rather than another. In fact one played off the other. The comparative success of *Ready Salted Crips*, which was performed outside the college to a range of audiences, was an encouragement to try again a conventionally scripted play. The choice this time settled on Pinter's *The Dumb Waiter*. This allowed us to pursue a little further the notion that disability should be used as an integral and complementary part of the production. The play concerns the fortunes of two hired killers who find themselves awaiting fresh orders in a derelict kitchen underneath a restaurant. The orders to kill, mixed with orders for food, are transmitted via the dumb waiter which ascends to the restaurant above. The climax is reached when the order arrives to kill the next person to come into the kitchen. It transpires that this is one of the killers. The play ends as the one with the gun confronts the other, now stripped of gun, and with shirt undone, who appears as the victim.

The fact that the play's setting is pretty absurd and the characters themselves somewhat bizarre was a great help in deliberately playing up disability. In effect this only served to heighten the absurdity. In our production the actor playing Gus was in a wheelchair and the actor playing Ben was on crutches. The motivation for their actions is not immediately clear, and interpretation is in the hands of the director and the actors. We followed Pinter's stage instructions to the letter, except that instead of walking across, Gus wheeled across. He still stopped, took off his shoe, etc. The effect was arresting, and not, I would argue, in any way out of keeping with Pinter's intentions when writing the piece. Right at the start of the play disability was exploited thus (stage direction as follows):

GUS ties his laces, rises, yawns and begins to walk slowly to the door, left. He stops, looks down, and shakes his foot. BEN lowers his paper and watches him. GUS kneels and unties his shoelace and slowly takes off his shoe. He looks inside and brings out a flattened matchbox. He shakes it and examines it. Their eyes meet. BEN rattles his paper and reads. GUS puts the matchbox in his pocket and bends down to put on his shoe. He ties his lace, with difficulty. BEN lowers his paper and watches him. GUS walks to the door, left, stops and shakes the other foot. He kneels, unties his shoelace and slowly takes off the shoe. He looks inside it and brings out a flattened cigarette packet. He shakes it and examines it. Their eyes meet. BEN rattles his paper and reads. GUS puts the packet in his pocket, bends down, puts on his shoe and ties the lace . . . .

Perhaps the stage instructions that end the play are more easily understood and our use of them clearer. Ben receives an order through the speaking tube attached to the dumb waiter that the victim will be coming into their kitchen right away. Gus in the meantime is in the lavatory. Ben calls him and then:

> *(He takes out a comb and combs his hair, adjusts his jacket to diminish the bulge of the revolver. The lavatory flushes off left. BEN goes quickly to the door, left).*

BEN: Gus!

> *(The door right opens sharply. BEN turns, his revolver levelled at the door. GUS stumbles in. He is stripped of his jacket, waistcoat, tie, holster and revolver. He stops, body stooping, his arms at his sides. He raises his head and looks at BEN. A long silence. They stare at each other. Curtain).*

Again we followed Pinter's instructions, except that Gus came in not only stripped of his jacket as stipulated but out of his wheelchair. He crawled in. Our interpretation of that moment was that Gus was to be portrayed as totally vulnerable: a sacrificial offering. It seems to me that this is a good example of how disability can be used positively to reinforce a theatrical point.

Having performed *The Dumb Waiter*, our ambitions stretched to other works by authors such as Ionesco and Beckett. Ionesco's *Chairs* seemed an obvious possibility. But in fact more out of circumstance than intention our work tended to concentrate more and more on generating our own material. None the less, although there are still strong feelings that we should not be attempting work such as this, a policy document of the Graeae Theatre Company early in 1981 included Beckett's *Endgame* as a suggested production.

Our main reasons for not pursuing this course at the moment are, first, the technical limitations of actors with disabilities, and, second, the impetus that the successful productions of *Sideshow* gave us to explore further the theme of disability. Let me make clear that by 'technical limitations' I do not mean physical limitations as imposed by some handicap, but our lack of any training in stagecraft. I would accept that training does not have to be formal in the sense of attending a drama school, although it would be encouraging if such schools were slightly more ambitious in their admissions policy towards disabled applicants. Experience of a wide range of parts would be every bit as valuable, if not more so – but this is exactly what disabled actors lack. Unless they have acquired their disability after gaining experience, it is extremely unlikely that they will be able to get any other than the most peripheral of parts, or those calling specifically for a disabled actor. There *are* exceptions, where the actor has been able to persuade the director that a certain part could be played by a disabled person, but this is extremely rare, especially in the case of a visible disability. The one example known to me is Nabil Shaban, the co-founder of the Graeae Theatre Company. While at the University of Surrey he wheedled, browbeat and nagged his way into the parts of Hecate in *Macbeth* and Roderigo in *Othello*. But it takes a determined personality such as Nabil's to achieve this sort of recognition. Most disabled people would not be seen as having an equal opportunity with other actors at an audition.

Even the likelihood of disabled actors being cast as disabled characters is not good. If one thinks of some of the plays in recent years that have had as a central character someone with a handicap – and the list would include *Elephant Man, Whose Life is it Anyway? Duet for One, A Day in the Death of Joe Egg* – a disabled actor has appeared in none of them. Only *Children of a Lesser God* has specifically used a deaf actress. If one looks at TV and films, it is much the same story. Admittedly *Time Bandits* used dwarfs for main parts, but it would have been hard to envisage not doing so once the script was established. The universally popular R2-D2 in *Star Wars* was actually played by a dwarf, but that was because of economics of size rather than artistic initiative. One of the more successful actors, though often restricted in casting because he is a dwarf, is David Rappaport. More often than not he has been used in sketches and films for 'small person' jokes. But recently, apart from compèring an anti-nuclear-war fringe show, he has been appearing on ATV's children's show, *Tiswas*, as a presenter. This is important. It is his ability as a comedian that is being used, not the fact of his smallness.

However, casting directors are notoriously conservative. Nabil Shaban recounts the story of when he applied for an audition for the part of the Mekon in a proposed TV series on Dan Dare, the old *Eagle* comic hero. Having eventually tracked down the casting director and explained that he wished to audition for the part, the director rather apologetically said, 'We are actually looking for a midget.'

'I am a midget,' bellowed Nabil down the phone.

'Oh, you'd better come and see us then.'

Now in fact Nabil is not a midget, although he is very small. His medical condition, which in laymen's terms is a form of brittle bones, has left him with very small legs which are unable to sustain his weight. He is thus permanently in a wheelchair. So Nabil wheeled himself along. The casting director was completely taken aback by his presence. Nabil was similarly taken aback. The casting director was black.

Unfortunately, after much apologising the company was not prepared to take the risk of even auditioning him. The part was considered 'too physically demanding'. In the meantime, Nabil has got work in TV but, as yet, only in disabled roles.

At present there are precious few channels other than the Graeae Theatre Company whereby a disabled person with aspirations to act can find any experience at all. The present full-time company, which consists of five actors, has gained an immense amount just by performing in front of a variety of audiences in a variety of venues. But it very quickly became apparent that, although enthusiasm and *joie de vivre* could sustain a show for a couple of performances, greater exposure demanded a certain acting competence. The act of performance is perhaps the greatest education. Once the initial fears of forgetting or missing out words or making wrong moves are over, then the real problems of acting start to emerge. The actor has to start working at his abilities to communicate, to analyse whether he is playing in a way that actually assists the production and his fellow actors. And this is all part and parcel of growing into and understanding the part that he is playing.

Audiences, of course, act as monitors to performance. But they are not always that reliable, and they are clumsy in that they are likely to deal in ultimates: 'That was good' or 'That was bad' might be typical reactions. It is an unqualified gut reaction. And it does tend to be about the content of the play rather than its performance. Of course, in the actor's mind the two are inextricably linked, with an emphasis, if at all, on the performance.

In the first show that was ever toured, which was *Ready Salted Crips* in 1974, some attempt was made to gauge audience reaction by encouraging written comment. The performance was at the Mid-Warwickshire College of Further Education in Leamington. The audience consisted of young people who were the peer group of the performers. It was a press-ganged audience in that it was a compulsory part of the General Studies programme for that day. The lecturer responsible followed it up in further lessons and sent me a copy of the student feedback!

Three general reactions were noted by staff running follow-up classes.
1. Sympathy evoked towards problems of handicapped people. Appreciation of efforts. An 'eye-opener' to different types of handicap.

2. Opposite reaction, i.e. regarding these people as not normal, therefore out of the mainstream. They sympathised with the bus conductor (in a sketch where a disabled person's speech defect produced consternation in a bus). They disbelieved that a spastic girl had two 'A' levels, etc. This group were more understanding towards the girl injured in an accident because she had once been 'normal'.

3. Dislike at seeing handicapped people; two of the class left the building as soon as they saw what was in store.

   No one said they found the sketches humorous, but most reported it as being 'all right'. Many thought they were being 'got at' in a rather unfair way; the thing that really shook a couple of them was the bit about not wanting charity, and the rude words about the 'plastic spastic' (collecting boxes in the shape of young disabled children often found in shop doorways). They obviously like the idea of forelock-tugging gratitude in return for small change.

And here are some of the individual students' comments:

I didn't know when they were acting and when it was real. [Boy.]

It taught me a lot. [Several.]

I learnt more during that performance than I've learnt all year in college. I suddenly felt that I had started to think about other people. [Boy, eighteen.]

I thought the play was easy to follow and amusing. There was little acting in it, but it still produced the desired effect on the audience – it made me feel rather guilty and made me realise how little notice is taken of handicapped people. We tend on the whole to regard handicapped people, just because they are physically and mentally handicapped, as objects who are not as clever as us and we feel sorry for them. But I think the appeal of this play was, we are just as good and as human as you are.

The whole thing provoked a strong feeling of guilt and I felt that this was probably their intention.

I have always known that just because a person was physically handicapped it has no effect on them mentally. As I said, I have always known it but I don't think I realised it until I watched them. It's hard to explain, but somewhere at the back of my mind I still thought communication with ordinary people was impossible on an equal level. That was one problem the play straightened me out on. The students were obviously intelligent and far more able than I when it comes to using their acting talents. They proved to me that they were able to cope with the world they were born into but, above all, I left the room feeling very lucky indeed that I was not born handicapped.

Virtually all the comments refer to the content of the show. This range of views is standard and is reflected in the sort of remarks made now after a show, eight years later. The disturbing nature of the material still shocks, but it does not necessarily help refine the presentation, or develop the actors' craft. There are, of course, people experienced in theatre who make extremely pertinent points and who are of great assistance to the company. But there is still the underlying need to provide the experience and training. Graeae is in the process of establishing a series of workshops and training programmes with this in mind. Without this type of programme, the likelihood of Richard III being played by a hunchbacked actor or Long John Silver by a one-legged actor, is remote.

This chapter has tried to answer the question 'What form of theatre?' by outlining the various alternatives and the experiments so far undertaken. It should not be imagined that this was the result of any great plan. The rationale for the theatre company only emerged slowly as a result of trial and error. The refining of ideas and the light of experience were tending to point, at least in the first instance, towards developing our own material. *Ready Salted Crips*, the show devised at Hereward College, had progressed into *Sideshow* by the time I was at the University of Illinois in 1975/76. At the foundation of the Graeae Theatre Company in February 1980, *Sideshow* presented itself as a starting point. It existed as a script and had worked. With a fair amount of redrafting it could work again.

It was only with the need to develop a new show to succeed *Sideshow* in June/July 1981 that it became apparent that the process of working up our own material was much harder than we at first appreciated. *Sideshow* had looked at standard targets from the disabled person's point of view, and although all the sketches were rooted in the experience of a number of disabled people, the way they were portrayed, with the exception of the accident sequence, was not personal. It was a satire on generally perceived attitudes. One outcome of this was that the company felt distanced from the material. It no longer reflected their developing personal perceptions; it no longer fulfilled the original intention of providing a platform for disabled people to tell of their experiences. And so a new work that did this was contemplated. Our approach referred back to the original script of *High Dive*, but this time we were not going to confine it to the theme of disability. The play was *3D*.

We were, of course, not the only company working in this way. And especially not so in 1981, when many theatre-in-education groups were looking at disability as a theme. But we were attempting something far more complex and difficult, for here were five individual people with disabilities. The end result certainly did not simplify anybody's perception of disability. If anything it confused and contradicted it, and the audience. Maybe, because of that, it wasn't entirely satisfactory theatre in a conventional sense. It had no beginning, middle or end. It was merely a collection of stories from five people's lives.

This method of working immediately presented each of the actors with the problem of selection. What stories could they tell? Which ones put them in a good light? Which in a bad?

Perhaps the question that caused most anguish was 'Can I mention something that happened that is important to me, but which involves another person?' There is no answer to this sort of question. Only the individual can say whether he or she would wish to use the story, or have it used. Naturally the recalling of some stories caused distress. The one that remains most firmly fixed in my mind is the one I quoted in Chapter 1 – Elane Roberts describing the death of her father. She had no doubts beforehand about speaking about this in public, but when it came down to it she found that she got a block. She was holding back and found it difficult to even remember the lines. We held a rehearsal just for her in an attempt to break down the block, and this was successful in as much as the reality of her memory led her to weep. In the dress rehearsal she repeated this, only just managing to get through it. The effect was electric. The real emotion and tension made the hair on my neck stand on end. It was an unforgettable theatrical experience. And yet the nagging question emerged then, and was to do so later with speeches equally moving and distressing: was it fair? Was it not exploitation? Had I, as the writer-up of privately divulged experiences, or the director, any right to ask this sort of performance from an actor? The naive question, as presented by one student years previously, 'When is it real, and when is it acting?' became peculiarly pertinent.

The accusation of exploitation was one I levelled at myself at the very outset. Was there not an element of the freak show in any performance? Wasn't a deliberate displaying of disability demeaning for the actors? I am convinced that if any of the disabled people I have worked with had felt that, it would have been made very clear to me. But this new play was different, even though all the actors could and did sometimes exercise a veto on the nature of speeches just as I, as script-writer, sought to protect the style or the language of a speech.

This debate was epitomised in the production of a play called *Crutch* by Nigel Gregory. Although not a Graeae production, its working method was similar to that used for *3D*, discussed above. It also had Nabil Shaban as one of its leading actors. The script examined the relationship between two people – one, played by Nabil, an artist confined to a wheelchair, the other, a deaf arts administrator. The play was firmly founded on an experience in Nabil's life, though this was known only to the people who knew both parties. I have no idea as to its literal accuracy, although the whole thing rang very true. But it was performed without the consent, or even knowledge, of the other party. Again a moral dilemma. Does the public airing of a private and personal matter constitute exploitation? Certainly, opinions divided strongly on this. One would hold that it was an unforgivable invasion of individual privacy, while another would argue that the play should be judged on its merits. There is no easy answer to this, but it does indicate that the route chosen up to now by Graeae is peppered with pitfalls not necessarily associated with conventionally scripted plays.

Two important underlying principles have been discussed in this chapter: the first is to encourage the active participation of disabled people in exploring their aspirations and the second is to develop, for the time being, our own material. A third basic requirement is that of touring.

The first material as we have seen, was performed within a residential college of further education for physically handicapped school-leavers, so the audiences were fellow students, staff, relatives and friends. To test out any theory of disabled people performing theatre, it was obvious at a very early stage that productions had to be taken into the community. There had seemed to be no way of attracting the community into a special college of further education, but the development of a show like *Ready Salted Crips* allowed us to do just this. So we took it round various venues in Coventry. The first was the local college of education in Canley, Coventry. The evening went unexpectedly well – unexpectedly, because, working so close to a project, it was easy to forget the impact that the content could have. And the impact was considerable because most of the audience had never thought of disabled people as being funny, rude, outrageous or unpleasant. The college magazine review read as follows: 'The real triumph of the whole performance was that we quite forgot to feel sorry for any of the cast. They shook up our complacent attitudes, involved us in their problems and challenged us to be sympathetic if we dared.' We naturally thought we had a triumph on our hands. By contrast, there is nothing like a performance in front of a sparse and lukewarm audience to awaken one to the realisation that performance is hard work; the unfortunate Clive Wolffe from the National Students' Drama Festival was subjected to that experience at the University of Warwick. The one performance of *Ready Salted Crips* that lives in my memory was that at South Warwickshire College of Further Education, which ran a strong drama department who responded with generosity and enthusiasm. The performance was a delight.

That was in 1974, and it was not until 1980, when Graeae was formally founded, that the idea of touring reached fruition. Again circumstances influenced policy. Up until then, Nabil Shaban and I had often considered establishing a theatre company, but it was only when we received an invitation to attend and perform at the World Congress on Rehabilitation in Winnipeg, Canada, that we felt motivated to do something about it. When one has no theatre and no money, touring seems quite attractive as a cheaper alternative. As a run-up to the Canada trip, we fixed a few dates in this country and set about recruiting a company and reworking *Sideshow*.

The remarkable thing about the newly formed company was the dedication and the personal sacrifice in terms of finance and energy that its members were willing to make. Marion Saunders, accompanied by our future stage manager Barbara Warren, was prepared to travel weekly from Torbay in Devon. Will Kennen undertook to travel from Taunton in Somerset. The remainder of the company were nearer London, so travel was not quite so crucial. Nabil Shaban, Jag Plah, Elane Roberts and Alex Low now completed the acting company. Brenda Miller acted as costumier and stage manager. Rehearsals were conducted initially in a church hall in Highgate. This was unheated, down a flight of stairs, and with a stone floor. Not ideal conditions in February. Then the Royal Association for Disability and Rehabilitation (RADAR) lent us the Diorama in Peto Place, Regents Park, free of charge. It had no light, but it had some heating and it was accessible.

The money to travel to Canada resulted from the personal generosity of an old friend of mine, Michael Silver. The tour was now extended to include three weeks at my old Alma Mater, the University of Illinois. We gave three performances before we left – at the University of London and the Middlesex Polytechnic. This last gave us some idea of the different venues and problems that we were going to have to cope with in the future. It was in a bar, heavily populated with space invader machines and thirsty students. The fact that the performance did not die redounds upon the guts and determination of the actors. It was a tough and significant baptism. And so, in all innocence, we flew to the United States.

The problems of travel and accommodation for a company made up largely of disabled people can be horrendous. Graeae has plenty of gruesome stories, but America is certainly not one. We stayed at the University of Illinois for three weeks, in a hall of residence that was totally accessible. We had the use of a bus specially adapted with hydraulic lifts and driven by charming and helpful drivers. The usual inconveniences of disability were not nearly so prevalent in Illinois. That gave us the opportunity to work at performance. And work we did. In the twenty-four days that we stayed there we gave twenty-seven performances – sometimes two a day, and on two memorable occasions it was three a day. We played every imaginable venue, from churches to the open air, from a bank to school halls. We played to all sorts of audiences – medical students, Presbyterian ministers, senior citizens, children and so on. The very act of work itself instilled a discipline and an understanding of audiences that we could not have achieved any other way.

Problems of technique became immediately apparent. Most of the company's voices were weak and uncontrolled. In the case of Jag, a slight speech impairment complicated delivery. But speaking in the open air against a stiff breeze to a sparse audience concentrates markedly the wish to communicate. Experience taught us some idea of pace, and some idea of pointing lines. It was all very haphazard, but with every performance we learnt. Performances grew in stature, and what had been an under-confident, hesitant company gradually emerged as self-confident and competent. In the bus on the way back from a theatre performance, we asked one of our drivers, who had seen the show for the first time, 'Fergie, what did you think of it?' Fergie turned to us and with a tear in his eye said, 'You people are beautiful. Just beautiful.' It was probably the biggest compliment ever paid to the company.

The coordinator of our programme in Illinois was Eden Nicholas. In his full-time capacity Nick was the local representative for the vocational rehabilitation programme. But he had once been a professional actor, and was still heavily involved in amateur productions throughout the state. His support and advice were invaluable, even if he did get us engagements in the most outlandish places. However, our most important performance was to be at the prestigious Krannert Arts Centre. The University of Illinois is fortunate to possess this incredible facility. It is a complex of five theatres, including a festival hall for concerts, an enormous proscenium arch theatre and a studio theatre. We were allocated the studio theatre for one night. The date fixed was Friday 13th. The whole of our tour had been building up to this, with TV and radio coverage.

I suppose we were all at the time challenging our luck. We had set off for the USA without enough money in reserve to pay for medical treatment, or to fly anyone back in an emergency.

On Thursday 12th we were in a bar for the evening, and by the time we left it was Friday 13th by an hour or so. Elane, who is blind, was pushing Nabil in a wheelchair. I heard a cry from behind me – 'Nabil has fallen out of his chair.' Now the last time that Nabil had fallen out of his chair he had broken his thigh and fractured his skull. He had been in hospital for three weeks. So I turned back expecting the worst, in the full knowledge that we could not play at the Krannert without Nabil.

He was lying in the middle of the road smiling happily.

'What have you broken?' I said.

'I don't think I've broken anything.'

'Come on. What have you broken?'

'I don't think I've broken anything.'

Amazingly, it was true. For the first time Nabil had fallen out of his chair and had broken nothing, although he did have some reservations about a toe. The fact that he was outside several vodkas had probably helped.

We played at the Krannert to a packed audience and a rapturous response. One review went as follows: 'Some theatrical experiences are without precedent, so special that we forever feel gratitude for having taken part in them, even if only as members of the audience. Such was my response to the appearance of Graeae, a troupe of disabled actors from England who presented *Sideshow* in the studio theatre at the Krannert last Friday night, regrettably for only one performance.' And there was much more in similar vein, which was extremely encouraging for all of us. I am absolutely certain that if we had not been worked so hard just before this performance we would not have achieved the same success.

In a euphoric glow we set off for Canada for one performance at the World Congress on Rehabilitation in Winnipeg. We quickly learnt that the living conditions we had experienced in Illinois were the exception and not the rule. Transport was cumbersome; loading up could take twenty minutes. Accommodation – we had been put up for the first night in a notorious red-light district hotel (inaccessible) – was miles out of town. Even so we managed sufficient publicity to play before an audience of more than seven hundred people. Again we were very pleased with ourselves. We had to perform on an improvised stage, with minimum lighting and bad acoustics. But we had a tumultuous reception and, on the strength of it, although we were only scheduled to do one performance, we managed to organise another.

We came down to earth with a bump. Only about fifteen people turned up. It was a most salutary lesson. So older, and a little bit wiser, we returned home, only to lose all our costumes and props in transit for over two weeks.

But now the real touring began. We had worked hard in the USA and the performance had benefited hugely. In Canada we had started to experience some of the realities of touring life. In England we were to live those realities to the full, what with vehicles breaking down, accommodation failing to materialise, company members falling ill and so on. But from June 1980 we kept on touring most weekends. We played Torbay and Exeter, Brighton, Cambridge, Cardiff, Wantage, Oxford, Reading, Southampton. We would play anywhere for anyone who asked us. So in Cardiff we played in the lovely Sherman Theatre. In Reading we played at the university in a room with a rock band next door. In Torbay we played at the tiny Bijou Theatre where to move three wheelchairs on stage was virtually impossible.

Eventually we came to London to play at the Soho Poly for a week. Now the Soho Poly is tiny, seating only some fifty people at best; it is also down a flight of steps with a ninety-degree turn half-way down. However, the Soho Poly was a crucial experience. Although one performance was given to an audience of five, consisting of the mother and father of the stage manager, a friend of one of the company, and my daughter and a friend, another performance brought a reviewer from the *Guardian*, who wrote us up very positively. We suddenly got taken up by the media.

But the story of Graeae and the media is not really appropriate for this chapter. What I have been trying to demonstrate is that touring became an integral part of Graeae's style. It taught us that if people want to do something badly enough they will always find the necessary stamina, and that handicap is no hindrance to aspiration and hard work. I shall not forget borrowing a meat van from the long-suffering Michael Silver to drive to Cardiff for an engagement, and literally throwing Marion in to lie on her back for the initial stage of the journey. All she said was, 'Oh well, it's a new experience.' I shall not forget Will who, having missed one performance because he had just had an epileptic fit, turned up at the next as if nothing had happened. I will not forget Elane who refused to make a fuss about losing a contact lens while we were in Winnipeg, and indeed did not comment on it for nearly a week, although she was suffering considerable irritation and pain.

Constant touring demands careful planning. There is a marked difference in the spirit of the Graeae Company – which now spends most of its time touring – and indeed in their performance, if they have travelled in some comfort and can stay in reasonable accommodation. Given that between July and December 1981 they gave well over a hundred performances in over sixty different venues, it is not unreasonable to demand some sort of comfort. I find it ironic that the Royal Shakespeare Company, doing a far less extensive tour in 1980, complained vociferously about their conditions. They would have to be made of sterner stuff to tour with Graeae.

Touring also allows the company to go where conventional theatre might never go, and it allows performance to be coupled with a workshop. So it is not unusual for the company to run a workshop at a day centre or adult training centre in the afternoon, and then give a performance that evening. Graeae is in the business of educating and enlightening people. To do this, it is essential to take on virtually any engagement.

Touring is only part of Graeae's work. I turn now to the more overtly teaching work in which the company is engaged.

3: Education

Teaching in Schools and Centres

The act of putting on shows about disability, performed by disabled people, is in itself an education for an audience. However, the experience of playing to young people in school convinced the company that the standard shows in their repertoire were not in themselves sufficient. Such shows introduced certain concepts which, if a question and answer session followed the performance, could be developed, but often the discussion was general and anecdotal. We felt strongly that the company's responsibility was to introduce more explicit discussion on disability.

Our starting point was one section of the play *3D*. As I have explained in the last chapter, this play was developed from individual and personal experience. A part of that experience relates specifically to disability, and the attendant script is a writing up of improvisation.

The company at this stage consisted of the following: Nabil Shaban – in a wheelchair as a result of osteogenesis imperfecta; Elane Roberts – blind; Yvonne Allen – with thalidomide-induced limb deficiencies, and in an electric wheelchair; Jag Plah – cerebrally palsied, using crutches; Deniz Bulli – partially sighted. The improvisation consisted of putting each member of the company on stage and asking them, 'Tell me about blindness', or 'What exactly is it like spending most of your time in a wheelchair?', or 'What does it mean to you being a spastic?' The results were fascinating.

This, more or less, is the bones of what Elane said:

I'm going to take you on a sense journey. The only sense that
I will not be using very much is that of sight. At first sight –
and don't worry about using words like that to a blind
person – at first sight this journey may seem mundane, but
we'll see how we get on. I'm going to make a cup of tea for a
friend who's ill upstairs. And I'm going to be in a kitchen
that I don't know. So here goes. I stop just inside the door.
I'll listen to see if anyone's here. 'Hello.' There's nobody
here, nobody's spoken. What was that? Something pushed
past my legs. Must have been a dog. They always worry me a
bit. I'll put my hands out to feel what's there. I don't like
doing that when someone else is there. It seems such a blind
thing to do. I'll work my way round to see what's here. I'm
really looking for the kettle. This is a work surface. The
kettle could be here. Is there a plug? Can't find one. Ah,
here's the cooker. If it's a gas cooker, it could easily be on the
cooker. Let's see. Ah, yes, here it is. Now, what we need is a
sink. I'll put the kettle down again to leave both hands free.
There's light over there, I wonder if that's a window. The
sink could be under that. Maybe it's over here. Yes, got the
sink. Right, taps. So I'll go back and get the kettle. Cooker,
hands down, and across, it's back there somewhere. Got it.
Back to the sink. Is this draining board clear? Yes, put the
kettle down. Right, the taps. See if the letter is indented in
the top. Yes, it is. This is the cold tap. Fill the kettle. Is that
enough? It feels heavy enough. Back to the cooker. Hell's
teeth, what's that? Bowl of something. The bloody dog. I
forgot about that. That's one reason for disliking dogs. Now
the cooker. I wonder if there are any matches around. Must
keep an eye open for that dog coming back. Ah, on the side,
here we are. Matches. I don't like gas cookers, because I
never know which tap is on. I don't know where to light it.
Here goes. Knobs down here. Let's turn this one and see
what happens. Listen for which one. I think it's this one.
Strike a light. No. Match finished. Try another. Right.
Good. Turn it up full. Put kettle on. Now what we need is
the teapot and tea. I wonder if it's on the work surface here.
No. What's this? Not tea. A jar of something. Oh, it's

macaroni. The little shells. Another big jar. Doesn't feel like tea. Try here. What's in this? Oh, a caddy. Sounds possible. Mmm! Tea. Need the teapot, wonder if it's on the tray. That jar must be for coffee or something. What's here. Ah, teapot! Bet they don't use it. Anything inside? No, it's clean. Right, got to wait for the kettle to boil. Now find the cups. Wonder if they're in the cupboards down here. No, a tin of something, a packet of something. No. Food, down here. Definitely the food cupboard. Possibly it's the other side of the cooker, or are there overhead cupboards? Yes— door open, could have brained myself on that. Ah, cups. I want two. All we need is milk. I haven't found the fridge yet. I wonder if it's along this wall. Ah yes, it should be in the big compartment in the door. No compartment. Must be by the freezer. Agh, what's that? Smells like cat food. God, a dog *and* a cat. Lucky not to have broken a leg. Yes, there's a bottle here. It's got a top on, it feels right. Shake the bottle, press the top in and hold it. Pour it in. It's a full bottle, don't have to tip too far. Guess the amount. Put top back on. Back to the fridge. Kettle's boiling. That's the knob turned up. Turn it down. Kettle's got a reinforced handle, so I don't need a cloth. Here's the teapot. Warm it. Kettle's got a difficult spout. Swish it round. Into the sink. Mind the dog bowl. Back again. Tea caddy. Has a spoon in it. One, two. Where's the kettle? Pour it in. Is it full? Put the finger in. Yes, full enough. Kettle down. Lid back on teapot. Oh, I forgot the sugar. Now there was a jar of something over here. Possibly. Open it and see. No, that's coffee. Ah, a jar back here. Don't know, taste it. Oh definitely sugar. Need a spoon. Drawers along here. Look in here. Paper. What about here? This is cutlery. Forks. Spoons other end? Yes. Sugar here. Cups. [She takes one spoonful.] That feels about right. Put lid on sugar before I forget. Tea should be ready. Gosh, it's hot. Stick my finger down the side and make sure I don't spill it. One cup. There we have the other cup. So there we have it. A cup of tea. Anyone for tea?

This whole routine, as written here, is very disjointed and at times monosyllabic. But if you can imagine the whole activity, it takes on a different, and dynamic meaning. Little phrases reverberate in the mind. How many people have considered that tea has a sound? And yet whether something 'sounds like tea' is of importance to Elane. The details that confront a blind person every day of his or her life suddenly become real and, vicariously, the audience can begin to share that experience.

There were many approaches open to Elane in developing material on blindness. She was particularly interested in introducing the sense of touch to the audience, so that they could concentrate on it. This is how she introduced her talk on making tea:

> I rely an awful lot on touch. I use my touch to read material – braille. I use it to find objects. It is the prime replacer of sight. I feel things, getting up in the morning. I can feel the sun. I put my hand out of the front door and see if it's raining. Oh, by the way, never worry about using the word 'see' with people who can't. It's a normal part of the vocabulary. I use it all the time. Touch is pleasurable. I can't see a picture or a landscape, but I can touch things. Textures of clothes. I love mohair. Touching people. I know we're not a very touchy people, but it can be very pleasant. You should try just concentrating on touching your own or somebody else's hand. Concentrate on what it really feels like – the smooth bits – the rough bits. Is it warm, is it pleasant to the touch?

She has now developed this particular section to the extent that she no longer explains how to make a cup of tea, but tries to get the audience to experience touch in a more immediate way.

Touch had been the subject of some debate because we were attempting to give an audience a 'real' experience. But how to do it? The first suggestion was that every member of the audience should be given some stones, which could be used for a tactile experiment. The administration of this seemed far too complex, and likely to descend into anticlimax, if not farce, with stones being dropped or lost. The next suggestion was that an audience should have a more physical experience. One idea was that each member of the audience should feel the face of their neighbour. We decided that this should be done with all the lights out. We were aware that embarrassment, giggling and a certain anxiety would all be part and parcel of the experience. So this is what Elane now does when in a theatre. She discusses touch as an important information gatherer, and then has all the lights turned out and talks the audience through feeling the face of their neighbour. She encourages people to trace the shape of the nose or the chin, to feel the texture and heat of the skin. Then she calls for the lights to come up and asks questions. 'What did that feel like?' 'Have you ever done that before?' This usually encourages a response of some sort. Elane's handling of this is also interesting: she has to explain that there is no point in holding up your hand if you want to say something. She can't see it. You have to call out.

Now this particular scene is only used in a theatre where there are lights and where actor and audience are clearly defined. In a school it can become more informal and, depending on the members, far more participatory. There are specially adapted spectacles that can simulate certain eye conditions, such as tunnel vision or glaucoma. There are blindfolds to enable people to experience total vision loss, and to find out what it's like to be led round by a sighted helper. All the time Elane is talking, answering questions, asking questions. In the end the group's experience is much greater than would result from a formal lecture on blindness. Hopefully the new understanding helps dispel some of the mystery of blindness and the awe in which blind people are often held. It may even give the chance to impart some information. It is a surprise to many people to realise that 'blindness' is a term that does not necessarily mean 'without sight'. Elane is blind, but she can distinguish light and dark, bright colours and vague shapes. I have seen expressions of some disquiet on observers' faces when they have witnessed Elane commenting on a pair of brightly coloured shoes worn by a company member.

Deniz expands the range covered by the term blindness by talking about partial-sightedness and its associated problems. Here are his initial comments:

Now let me tell you how much I can actually see. Many of you will be wearing glasses and if you take them off that may give you some idea. But glasses will make no difference to me, and although I can read I have to use this device to magnify the print. It's not just an ordinary magnifying glass, it's up to five times' strength. I also have a monocular aid for long distances. Here it is. I use it to look into the changing room at the police station next door to my home. What those boys get up to! Anyway, let me see. I can see that you are the audience, or more specifically I can hear that you are there and I can also smell you are there. Now don't be offended, smell is very important to me. I use it a lot. When I enter a room I can't see it clearly, so I have to let all the other senses give me information. What the carpet smells of, whether there's dust, tobacco, people. I use touch as well. When I buy clothes I pick them by touch – soft, warm, rough, smooth, nice against the skin – my colour sense is a little haphazard. Now let me see, I know you are the audience, so that means you're male and female, probably. I can't tell which. Let me come a little closer. Right. I know there are people there. Individuals. But I still can't tell if you are male or female. A little closer. Well, I think you're a man/woman, because of the way you're sitting and the length of your hair. Don't be offended if I'm wrong. I'll get a little closer. Ah, you see I'm right/wrong. Your face is just a white blob, I'm afraid. I'm sure there's a nose and a mouth and eyes there somewhere. I'll have to get up really close. I used to work in a beauty salon and I had to ram my nose right against somebody's cheek to get it right. Now there we are, I can see you quite well. It was well worth it, wasn't it? [Kisses him/her.] I have to get that close, if I'm to see what you really look like. It wouldn't matter if I was looking at an object. A cup or a plate. But because it's a person I'm invading their space, their privacy. So I have to get pretty familiar with people before I can get much idea of them visually, and the face and particularly the eyes are so important if you want to know somebody. But imagine what it's like walking around town at night. Crossing roads is pretty hazardous. I get very confused. All the different lights, car headlights, tail lights, road lights, belisha beacons. When it's wet, the reflection. The glare. I find distances hard. How near is that car, or is it a lorry? Can I cross now? Sound doesn't tell me much if there's a lot of traffic around. Should I chance it? There seems to be a lull. Here goes. Well, I made it that time. But late at night it's people who can be dangerous. And I just can't tell, you see. I rely on vibes. What people feel like. When I see a group of people together I get very wary. I probably throw out all sorts of aggressive feelings anyway. And I tense up. I suppose if you look gay or are wearing clothes that are a little unusual, you are asking for it. But I don't see why people should dictate to me what I should wear or how I should act. Anyway, I'm very wary. Who is this group? Are they skinheads looking for bother, or are they just people coming home from the pub? Will they notice me? I hope to God they ignore me, and just pass by. The shadows are large. How many of them are there? I can't tell. Are they big? Are they all fellers? I can't tell. They're noisy. Laughing. I tense up. My fists clench. I get ready for anything. Have I got something sharp in my pocket? I'll take one of them with me. Christ, they're slowing down, aren't they? They've noticed me. Please God let them just walk. They've called my name. Oh my God. They're friends. You bastards. What a dirty trick to play. You knew I couldn't see you. That sort of thing is really unpleasant. I've been caught more than once and really done over. When it happened last I reported it to the police. 'Are you queer, then?' is about all they said. They felt I deserved it, I suppose. Anyway, I went home, put on all my make-up and my most outrageous clothes and went out again. You can't let the bastards get you down.

The other fact that can be a greater handicap to Deniz is that people, just by looking at him, will often assume he is gay. Deniz does wear make-up and at times dresses a little outrageously. As he describes above, that can be positively dangerous. Given that he is also partially sighted, Deniz is doubly vulnerable. But, as he says, he doesn't see why people should dictate to him what he wears or how he looks. In most social situations Deniz will appear to cope extremely well. He has worked out a series of strategies so that any hesitation or slight mishap can be passed off easily without betraying the state of his vision. Elane, in an earlier speech, talks of how she cultivated 'vagueness' when she was losing her sight, so that people wouldn't notice. Now, as a blind person, she has no hesitation in using a white stick when in a strange environment. Deniz has no use for such a device, because for the most part he can operate perfectly adequately in the street. And, in fact, a white stick would not give him the sort of information that would save him from the kind of confrontation he describes in his speech.

When Elane's and Deniz' pieces are played together, they not only give an audience a much greater insight into visual handicap but they also encourage the airing of apprehensions and prejudices in the secure knowledge that no one will take offence or find any fear or question ridiculous.

Two other members of the company talk about living most of their waking life in a wheelchair. Yvonne, who was born with all four limbs severely affected by thalidomide, speaks of her experiences and feelings:

When I was a baby I used to hate wearing a nappy. I'd roll away so that my mum couldn't put it on me. I thought it a great laugh to roll under the table so that she couldn't get me. But having a nineteen-year-old bouncing about the floor is something different. Then I had my artificial legs and arms at one stage. After the first fun of a new toy I think we all hated them. I don't know a single person who is thalidomide who uses artificial arms or legs. So as soon as I left school, I threw them away. I had this dream of me and some of the other girls doing a strip routine. Except instead of clothes, we were ripping off our arms and legs. They looked real. You couldn't see the join. We were roaring with laughter. Sounds a bit sick really. So I use a chair, since I discarded my legs, except I haven't got arms to push myself, so I use crutches. They were specially developed so that I could push myself around. I can put the brakes on with them, see? I also have an electric chair. It's very neat and fast, but the battery has to be re-charged every night. The cost of these is about £1,000. One neat trick is getting up kerbs. This chair has kerb climbers, as they're called. Those things on the front. So here's a kerb. I should get up it without any help. Here goes, will she do it? [She mounts kerb and pirouettes centre rostrum.] No trouble. Now turn round to get down. There we are. The only problem is that if the kerb is more than four inches then the chair won't make it.

It does help to have help at times. Getting money out of my purse – it's easier if someone else does it. But I can do my make-up myself. You'd be surprised how much I can do. See this stick. This is really useful. Helps me get dressed, do up buttons; you see I haven't got much of a reach, so this acts as an extension. Pulls the choke out on my car, moves the pieces on a chess board, switches on lights, scratches my head, picks my teeth. This is a hair brush. Dead simple, isn't it? Usually I don't need any help looking after myself, getting dressed or going to the loo. But wearing a bra is a real pain. I've tried all sorts of ways of getting the bloody thing on. I feel very vulnerable, because I haven't got arms to protect myself. Boys take advantage. Sometimes I wish I had the damn things cut off. But I love discos, jiggling about in my chair. People do come and dance with you. There was this bloke who fancied himself as very macho. So he picks me up out of my chair to dance with me. Result was my knicker elastic broke and my knickers fell on the floor. He collapsed flat on his back with me on the floor. That gave him a hernia. The bouncers thought he was assaulting me so they picked him up and threw him down ten steps. Poor sod.

Adolescents readily identify with Yvonne's self-deprecating humour and can laugh at her anecdotes. The ice is broken and she can then easily lead a group into not just a question and answer session but into the practicalities of helping someone in a wheelchair. She can advise them on how help should be offered, as well as the techniques they can use. If a person is not used to pushing or lifting a wheelchair, they often find it comes apart in their hands, much to their embarrassment. Yvonne can instruct in an atmosphere of mutual trust and communication.

Nabil gives another viewpoint of life in a wheelchair:

You can look upon a wheelchair as a horse if you like. You can take pride in it. Brush its coat, comb its mane, make sure it's well shod and properly looked after. I don't give a damn about my chair. Partly because at school we were told to look after our wheelchairs, partly because it isn't mine, it belongs to the National Health system, and partly because it's the symbol of disability. You've all seen the access sign using a wheelchair as a logo. If you're disabled you are in a wheelchair. Still, it is pretty useful. It is my only means of getting about. It is my symbol of freedom. If I didn't have it, I'd be stuck on the floor crawling, so I suppose it deserves some respect. I look upon it as my throne. The uncrowned King of Jordan. I don't really need this cushion but it's a safety barrier. Protects me from falling out of my chair, or from banging into things, and I can use it as a tray. It also disguises the shape and size of my legs. People don't realise how small I am. The wheelchair is scaled down to my height. You get a very strange view of the world. All groins, bums and navels. People don't know if they should bend down or kneel down to talk to you. I suppose it embarrasses them as they must feel they're talking to a child. Whenever I go to a party, which isn't very often, I head straight for the wall. And as near to some chairs as possible. If people want to talk then they've got somewhere to sit down. It's a great temptation not to communicate, when somebody's up there you can't exactly catch their eye. About all you can do is bite them on the kneecap. But at least in a chair people can identify a need quickly. They can help you up a kerb or through a door. I don't mind being helped at all. When I'm pushing myself outside, I don't mind somebody giving me a push. Saves a lot of effort on my part. When you're low down there are all sorts of problems. Telephone boxes (I mean you can't reach the telephone, but that doesn't really matter – you can't get in), letter boxes, or visiting friends who live up steps, and even if there is a lift the buttons are invariably too high. However, it makes you think a bit. I got locked in a house once. The door handle was too high for me to reach. There were two steps down from the front door and there was a sort of grating between the bottom step and the pavement. This was real James Bond stuff. I got a broom to bang the top bolt open. I got on the floor from my wheelchair. Folded it up and knocked it over. I crawled down the stairs, pulled the chair after me and over the grating. Got back in it. Success! But the door was still open. So I searched round and found a piece of wood with a nail in it. I hooked it through the letter box. Banged the door and shoved the whole thing through the letter box. Voila! It took about half an hour and I was knackered.

Finally there is the presentation made by Jag. His cerebral palsy has affected his speech to some extent, and he also has an Indian accent. It takes some concentration to understand him perfectly – of which Jag is fully aware:

You probably found me difficult to understand at first. Come on, own up. I'll bet when I first opened my mouth you all thought, 'Oh no, it's one of them.' Well, not one of them. But one of them others. The ones from the funny farm. Everybody thinks I'm stupid. It makes me think it sometimes. When I walk down the road, people think, 'He's mad', but I don't feel weird. It's just part of being a spastic, I guess. And when I talk it makes perfect sense to me. I can understand every single word I say. Clear as a bell. Once I heard myself on TV and I couldn't understand a bloody word. And I knew what I was saying! It's difficult for people to take me seriously. I walk a little funny. I talk a little funny. So people believe I think and behave a little funny. My face doesn't help. Sometimes I smile or laugh when I don't mean to. So when I say something serious I can suddenly start laughing. I don't know why, it just happens. So people don't know how to take me. Some people don't even try. It takes a little concentration and effort to understand me. You are doing very well. I don't mind people saying, 'I'm sorry, I didn't understand; could you say it again!' At least it means they are trying to understand. Do you like my crutches? I decorated them myself. They give you these sad and naked sticks when you come out of hospital. They make you feel crippled. So I decorated them. People come up and say, 'Oh I like your sticks', so you can get talking. I've decorated my car too. I've got one of those blue invacars. We call them 'Noddies' or 'spas wagons'. I've got stickers on that say, 'King Jag' and another that says, 'The disabled are people.' Under that I wrote, 'And for my next joke'. You see, you don't know whether to take me seriously or not.

Jag has developed his routine so that he now demonstrates self-defence using his crutches on some hapless volunteer from the audience. This usually works very well and is very entertaining. Only on one occasion was Jag totally nonplussed, and that was when he selected from the audience someone who was blind. But the incident did little harm to the basic argument that the disabled can be positive and articulate and, in this instance, occasionally at a loss.

I have used various examples here from a scripted piece. It is not difficult to see how they can be used as an introduction to a workshop in which individual handicaps can be discussed freely. The aim is to increase knowledge and dispel prejudice. In practice it is remarkably easy to achieve this, provided the individuals leading the workshop have the self-confidence and experience to control and advance the session.

The potential for this approach is also clear. One can imagine a deaf actress conducting a series of workshops on communication, which would necessitate everybody learning some form of sign or mime language. One possible ramification of this could be the inclusion of deaf children in a hearing class, as well as a deepened understanding of non-verbal communication.

Graeae has only scratched the surface of the potential of this approach. The company is still exploring themes rooted in the individual's experience and situation, but not necessarily specific to handicap. For example, Deniz is preparing a series of workshops on 'body image'. This is important to him, and it relates to his experience of partial sightedness. But it could easily lead into discussions and improvisations on advertising, fashion, racism, and so on. It is almost impossible for the company to stay rigidly on the subject of one handicapping condition. They all have spin-offs that will be within the experience of the young people who make up the workshop. One of the great discoveries is that differences between a disabled person and an able-bodied person are limited, and that the similarities of experience and opinion are very much more fundamental. If that and that alone is the conclusion of a workshop session, then it has been a session well spent.

Teaching within Graeae
In the last chapter I commented on the inadequacies and unavailability of training for disabled people. The opportunities to learn about improvisation, or running a workshop, or contributing to a performance, are just not there. It is a central Graeae commitment that they should be there, and Graeae will do its best to provide them. This applies to any disabled person who is interested, and for the period of the workshop of course all those present become members of Graeae.

As yet there have only been three or four such sessions, the longest being a weekend course. But a three-week residential summer school is proposed which will have places for a dozen candidates and will be staffed by appropriately qualified and experienced drama teachers. The reaction of such teachers is, at first, apprehension; although experienced in teaching drama, they often feel inadequate to teach disabled people. But one can argue that their prime responsibility is no different from being confronted with any other group of willing, enthusiastic but ignorant beginners. Some of the techniques and exercises will have to be adapted, or new ones devised, but aims and objectives remain the same.

This is easy to say, and it can also look easy. But apprehensions and fears take some allaying. I recall watching an improvisation based on Weiss' *Marat-Sade*. The lecturer was interested in expressing the experience of institutionalisation and the perception of handicap – in this case, mental illness. One member of his group was confined to a wheelchair because of cerebral palsy. If anybody could have contributed to an improvisation on handicap and institutionalisation, with authority, it was him. The lecturer, however, excluded him with some such phrase as, 'I think you'll be happier as an observer.' What he meant, of course, was that he, the lecturer, would be happier if this person was not involved. It is not immediately obvious that disability can be used positively, nor that disabled people have unique and positive contributions to make.

Of course, there are obvious differences. Movement is one. Wheelchairs are, of course, on wheels which move smoothly and without apparent effort. An actor in a wheelchair moves without apparently doing so; his head stays on the same plane. This has interesting possibilities. In one early revue I directed a Keystone Cops kind of chase, with all the performers in wheelchairs. Wheelchair movement can be a perfectly viable theatrical form; so can movement by means of crutches. Ungainly gaits make interesting shapes: movements are very strong and extreme. Unfortunately there is as yet no real interest in developing movement for people with unusual gaits. Present practice tries to make them seem more 'normal'. For example, wheelchair dancing is very often based on square or country dancing, and as such it can be effective. But as always with this aping of able-bodied behaviour, it looks clumsy and incompetent unless performed by physically competent paraplegics with good arms and balance. This is needlessly limiting. No matter how handicapped, people can express themselves in movement. But their abilities have to be channelled and made relevant to the music. I look forward to a genuine attempt at exploring spastic movement as a means of interpreting music.

Related to this is the way in which deaf actors have expanded the repertoire of sign language, so that mime and signing have become a valid theatrical form. Exaggerated theatrical signs have their part to play in communicating with an audience. An extension of this, as suggested by a deaf former member of Graeae, is that a pop concert could be signed, so that dance would be added to the convention of sign-mime (deaf people very often have no trouble in keeping in rhythm as the reverberation of the percussion and the bass can be felt through the floor). I look forward to seeing this. Movement is challenging and should give the inventive drama teacher endless possibilities to develop new and interesting techniques.

This is also true of voice production. Conventionally a voice teacher is working towards clear articulation, a wide vocal range, projection and a good timbre. If the actor in question has a severe speech disorder, then that approach is probably inappropriate. The aim is still to communicate, but the methods may be different.

I have tried two different approaches for performance. In one production of *Sideshow* a member of the company was a severe athetoid spastic. His speech was extremely difficult to understand. I was interested in exploring with all the company their experience and memory of recognising that they were handicapped. For Glen, there were two specific moments. The first was when, as a child, he used to play hide and seek with his able-bodied friends; he could never understand why he was always the first to be found. It suddenly occurred to him that it was much harder to hide himself in a wheelchair than it was for his friends. The second was when he heard his voice on his speech therapist's tape-recorder: this gave me the clue as to how we could get round the problem of relating these stories to an audience. It was a simple matter of reversal. The tape recorder became Glen's inner voice, expressing his feelings, using his words, but expressing them in clear speech. His own voice became the recorded voice, disjointed and difficult to comprehend. The device worked perfectly adequately.

Another device, used in the first instance as a joke, also worked effectively. A mock court room scene was to be played lampooning a job interview, with Glen as the defendant (see p. 83 *et seq.*). The judge complained that he couldn't understand what Glen was saying, so the prosecuting counsel inquired of the audience and the other players, 'Does anyone here speak spastic?' Not only did this get a laugh, but it also gave Glen the opportunity to express himself clearly through another person. This joke was extended to include some tension and disagreement between the defendant and the interpreter, and when as the punchline of the sketch the defendant told the judge to 'stick this job up his arse', the interpreter translated it as, 'He wishes to thank you for considering his application.' In one production this joke was made more complex as the interpreter was played by a deaf actress who signed the replies as well as spoke them. For the final line she said, 'He wishes to thank you for considering his application,' but signed, 'Stick this job up your arse.' As the sign for that is pretty graphic, the audience was in on the joke.

As with the problems of mobility, there are many exciting possibilities here. With one non-verbal man in a workshop, I toyed with the idea of using a flip chart of words or a TV screen. Ultimately one should be able to have synthetic speech (i.e. speech created by a machine.) In the meantime it is still possible to get over immediate problems by having two people playing one part. They could even be dressed in an all-enveloping costume.

Very often, for people with speech that is difficult to understand, the desire to communicate with another person is so strong that somehow the meaning, if not the individual words, gets through. I recounted earlier how a cerebrally palsied actor playing Confession in a morality play conveyed the meaning of his speech with probably no one in the audience actually recognising the words that he was using. Articulation and projection are important skills, but perhaps the crucial factor is the burning commitment that, no matter what, the audience is going to understand what is being said. It means that audiences do have to work hard, but communication is a two-way thing: one party has to listen. And in the case of understanding a severely handicapped actor, the act of listening is non-passive and a contributory part of the communication.

In this chapter I have outlined some of the methods that Graeae uses to explore issues in schools. I have also introduced some of the methods by which disabled people can be involved actively in workshop sessions. I believe strongly that these herald the start of a series of fascinating challenges and, I hope, brilliant solutions, that will allow disabled people more involvement in theatre and drama. I shall now discuss in more detail Graeae's workshop methods when running sessions for disabled as well as able-bodied groups.

4: Workshops

Graeae receives many invitations to run workshops, which the company see as an important and integral part of their function. Nevertheless, it is often difficult to prepare adequately, or to conduct a totally adequate session, when it is a once-and-for-all presentation. Any leader of workshops will be familiar with the standard problems of inappropriate space in institutions. Invariably the only available suitably sized room is the dining hall, which is next to the kitchen. The session is punctuated with meal preparation or washing up. And in conducting a workshop with handicapped people, individuals often have to be removed to another activity almost at the whim of the staff. Many institutions are ruled by the iron hand of the timetable and, in particular, the scheduling of transport. It is not unknown for irritated ambulance drivers to line the back of the hall, shuffling and coughing, determined to get their hands on their charges without another second's delay.

These are standard gripes, and they arise from the unwillingness or inability of the host institution to recognise that drama is as valid a part of the timetable as any other activity. Unfortunately, drama is still viewed as a kind of game that can be interrupted or ignored at will.

Having experienced these conditions, Graeae now attempts to lay down certain conditions. The first is that a session will be for a minimum of two hours, and that everyone shall be permitted to be involved for the whole period. The company also insist that there be no observers. Sometimes staff feel able to withdraw and not participate fully. They fall back on the slightly elitist argument that as 'professionals' they should have the opportunity to study their clients in a dramatic environment. The involvement of staff is usually extremely valuable in initiating and encouraging action, as well as giving the opportunity for them and their clients to be treated as of equal status for the purposes of the workshop.

It is made clear at the start of the session that not only is drama serious but that the material used will be generated by the group, and has to be treated seriously and with respect. Finally it is expected that at the end of the session there will be some sort of product – usually a sketch or a short scene.

One of the problems confronting Graeae at the moment is that it is rare to follow up a workshop with others, on a regular basis. It is also rare to be allowed more than a morning or an afternoon to develop themes. This lack of reinforcement and follow-through tends to make every workshop a 'special' event, rather than a regular and valued part of an institution's programme.

As I have indicated, Graeae find difficulty in preparing in advance an appropriate line to take. This is because the group for whom the workshop is to be run, is often inaccurately described. For instance, one will not take the same line with or make the same assumptions about a group of severely subnormal schoolchildren as one would in the case of physically handicapped adults. Elderly stroke victims will have different demands from young spinally injured patients. Very often the company only find out when they arrive about the make-up of the workshop group, and so a certain flexibility of approach is essential.

To give some idea of the approach used, here are two case studies of workshops, from which I afterwards attempt to draw some conclusions.

1 Illinois, USA, 1980

One of the very first workshops was held before the company had turned professional, while we were in Illinois. We had been invited to go to a school for severely mentally handicapped children for the morning, and to lead them in some sort of dramatic activity. At the time we had no idea what we should do or what to expect. We arrived at the school to find that they had been patiently waiting for twenty minutes in the main hall. There were some thirty young people aged between eleven and sixteen, and about as many helpers. This was a pretty awesome number to have to involve as actively as possible. At that stage we had only two tactics. One was to perform a little piece from the show; the other was to get everybody involved. None of us had had any experience in working with severely mentally handicapped young people and so we just had to plunge in.

At that time we had a song and dance sequence which incorporated two old faithfuls, 'Chatanooga Choo Choo' and 'By the Light of the Silvery Moon'. The company were dressed in brightly coloured costumes with straw boaters. The whole sequence took about two and a half minutes, and out of that we had to create something. 'Chatanooga Choo Choo' gave the clue: it started with the train whistle going 'whoo-whoo!' and we managed to get everybody doing that. The next step was obvious: we would create a train. I pulled the biggest boy in the group out on to the acting area, gave him a top hat and told him he was the station master. We had a green flag, and so it was now up to him when the train would leave the station. We then had to create a train and a station. A train is relatively straightforward when you have a number of participants in wheelchairs. We could then practise the train making a couple of circuits of the hall, and we put in some passengers. Fortunately we had plenty of hats to share out, and so gracious ladies could mingle with English boating types and Chicago gangsters.

However, we had used up only about half the assembled throng and we still needed a plot. Being in the USA provided the idea for that. We could have an Indian raid with lots of bloodshed and dramatic dying. The 7th cavalry would then ride to the rescue. That incorporated virtually all the remaining children except a few extremely handicapped young people who seemed to have little idea what was going on. They became signals, trees or mountains. In the end everyone was doing something and we ran through the whole scene twice to be sure we had some idea of what was supposed to happen. Amid great excitement we successfully concluded the scene with the arrival of the bugling 7th cavalry.

The exercise took about two hours and was really only a game. But, for many of the young people it was an important step that they actually participated and contributed without any form of disruptive behaviour. One can imagine building on this small scene to encourage a much greater range of participation and more sophistication in performance. One could have taken the Indians and explored dancing, painting and war paint, tracking and the various instruments of war. For the 7th cavalry one could have looked at uniform, drill, horses and so on. Every activity would lend itself to a programme that could become totally absorbing, and that would incorporate all the skills that a special school would wish to teach such severely handicapped youngsters.

As I describe it above, the session was very teacher/director orientated. At that stage it was very difficult to encourage the group to develop their own material. Not only was it far too big, but it contained many youngsters who were non-talkers. It would be necessary to have much smaller groups and for much longer, before experiences could be explored that would generate a sketch or even a script.

That afternoon the company took another group for a workshop, which was a considerable contrast to the morning. The group consisted of adolescent youngsters, mainly black, who were what in this country might be designated ESN(M) (mildly educationally subnormal). Several had been in trouble with the police and were now attending a form of summer camp whose main aim, as far as I could tell, was to keep them off the streets and out of mischief. There were about forty of them, with a dozen helpers. We did an excerpt from the show, as normal. The performance was enlivened by one of the larger members of the company slipping and doing what is known in the States as a 'prat fall'. The effect was such that everybody collapsed in laughter. At least the workshop had got off to a friendly start. This time we divided into three groups with the strict requirement to produce something at the end of the session.

One group – mine – worked on a discotheque scene in which a fight necessitated the calling of the police. Another created a playground and became various children's toys, such as bouncing balls and slides. The third group became a larger machine which with appropriate clunking and hissing whirred into life. One could not have imagined three more contrasting pieces.

At that time we had no set objectives. Merely surviving the two hours was sufficient. However, after each workshop there was a sense of elation and achievement that made the company recognise the value and importance of this work and the need to gain more experience and expertise.

2 Aberdeen, 1982

a) *The briefing*

The day before the workshop the director of Graeae, Nic Fine, held a briefing session. The following people were present: Deniz Bulli, Yvonne Allen, Jag Plah, Ellen Wilkie, Elane Roberts. Here is the discussion that ensued:

Nic: There will be fifteen disabled people and fifteen occupational therapists, so it's quite a range. As far as I know there are no deaf or blind people although there might be a couple with poor hearing and some degree of partial sightedness. The information is a bit vague, but it's unlikely the OTs will know the disabled people.

I think we should start as normal with an extract from *Sideshow* – the court room sketch. I'll introduce the scene, but I won't say much about Graeae, that can come later. I'll suggest some of the issues that the scene raises and describe the way the scene came about from rehearsal.

Now we must approach it like a performance. Don't start cold. Get yourselves prepared. We'll work in pairs. Shall I appoint?

Deniz: I'm very low on energy today. I'd prefer to work with someone who will be dominant.

Nic: Yvonne, would you like to dominate?

Yvonne: No, I'd prefer to share equally.

Nic: It's very rare that a workshop is shared equally. Right, Yvonne, you're working with Deniz. Ellen you work with Elane, I'll work with Jag. Don't worry, Yvonne, you'll handle it fine.

   One theme to explore is the relationship between the helper and the helped. Maybe try role reversals and explore any situation where someone is dominating others in a group. People might feel vulnerable, so it must be kept light.

Jag: Won't we be turning the disabled people against the OTs?

Nic: No. If you need help, you need it. It's how it's offered and how it's done that matters. Ellen and I did something similar at Leicester. It was quite heavy, and can be more powerful if it's funny. Remember that we got a stroke patient actually to teach a therapist to sing. If people can laugh at each other that'll be fine. Sketches on access and so on are so safe. We need to do something potentially more risky than that. Jag agrees.

Yvonne: I had a group once and nothing happened.

Nic: Battle on. I had that experience with old people and nothing happened. That's the risk.

Yvonne: If we get nothing do we set something up?

Nic: If after twenty to twenty-five minutes there's nothing, set something up. Become like a director. It's best of course if they develop it themselves. Keep the sketches to five minutes maximum. You must discuss with your partner who's going to do what. Try and limit discussion to fifteen minutes. People hide behind talking. When you come to do the sketch make sure it can be heard and seen. Try and structure the hour. We should finish up with a sketch. Even if it's a mess it doesn't matter.

Yvonne: Any danger of anyone being whisked away?
Nic: No, we've got a guarantee. Now let's rehearse the 'workshop chant'.
[They move into rehearsal.]

Various points emerge from this briefing that have been commented on earlier in the chapter. The company is not absolutely clear who will make up the workshop group. They have been informed that 50 per cent will be physically handicapped, but in the past this definition has included geriatric patients, elderly stroke patients and post-accident brain-damaged patients as well as congenitally physically handicapped people. All they can do is prepare a song routine and wait and see how it goes.

b) *The sketch*

Our hearts sink as we arrive at the day centre where the workshop is to take place. It looks as though the session is to be made up of severely mentally handicapped adults. What shall we do? This is followed by a certain amount of uncharitable relief when we realise that these are in fact the adult training centre trainees waiting to go home. We can go ahead as planned.

We go into the hall which doubles as a dining-room. Disabled people are already here, clustered at one end. The OTs come in later, rather hesitantly. We find they are students, mostly in their early twenties, rather than qualified practitioners. The disabled participants, on the other hand, are aged anything between eighteen and fifty. There is no immediate attempt by either group to mix.

Nic moves everybody in front of a playing area so that they can see the sketch that is to be performed. There are only a few people in wheelchairs. The biggest single disability group seems to be head injury. Nic underlines the point that everybody is participating by waiting for a couple chatting and then another couple who wander across the area as if not part of the session at all. As I said earlier, this casual assumption that drama workshops can be interrupted or walked through without any attempt at discretion is unfortunately common.

Nic then describes the court room scene and stresses the need for feedback afterwards.

Here is the sketch that was used.

JUDGE: Send in the defendant.
(Yvonne)
CLERK: Call Jag Plah.
(Elane)   Call Jag Plah.
(The defendant enters.)

PROSECUTOR: What is your name and address?
(Deniz)
DEFENDANT: Jag Plah, 16 Keith Road, Hayes,
(Jag)   Middlesex.
PROSECUTOR: I see. And what are your qualifications?

DEFENDANT: I have GCE 'O' level in maths,
swimming proficiency certificate and
driving licence.
JUDGE: What's that? Tell it to speak up a bit.
PROSECUTOR: *(To defendant)* Speak up a bit.
(To Judge) I would like to call my first
witness, by way of a referee. Miss Peabody,
teacher.
PROSECUTOR: Raise your right hand. Do you swear to tell
the truth, the whole truth and nothing but
the truth?
WITNESS: I do.
(Ellen)
PROSECUTOR: Now, Miss Peabody, can you give us your
testimonial as to the applicant's suitability
for this post?
WITNESS: He is extremely hard-working and
conscientious. His diligence has been
properly rewarded by his test scores and
exam results. This would indicate that he is
considerably above average intelligence.

	himself and has a pleasant, outward-looking personality.
PROSECUTOR:	One question, Miss Peabody. When the defendant took his tests did he have any extra time or help?
WITNESS:	He completed half his papers typing and the rest through the use of an amanuensis.
JUDGE:	Amanu – what?
WITNESS:	Amanuensis. It means dictating the answer to another person to write down.
JUDGE:	I see. Thank you.
PROSECUTOR:	Thank you. You may stand down. The next witness is the defendant's careers officer. Raise your right hand ...
COUNSELLOR: (Elane)	(*Does so and repeats oath.*)
PROSECUTOR:	You feel that a machine operator is a proper post for your client?
COUNSELLOR:	I certainly feel that he has a good chance of gaining and holding such a job. It has the added advantage of allowing me to close the file and turn the client into a meaningful contributing member of society.
PROSECUTOR:	I see. Thank you. My final witness is an old friend of the family. (*Repeats the swearing-in process.*)
FRIEND: (Ellen)	He is a good boy, your honour. I've known him since he was small. And he always worked so hard at his therapy and everything. I mean he's no fool. Look at his exam results. That's showed them, I said when I heard. That's showed them. And now all he needs is a chance. Just wait and see. Give him this chance and you won't regret it. I'm sure you won't. Just one chance, that's all.
PROSECUTOR:	(*Shuffles her out.*) Quite so. Now if I may turn to the defendant himself. How fast do

	you type?
DEFENDANT:	(*Replies none too distinctly*) What the hell has that got to do with being a machine operator?
PROSECUTOR:	What? What did you say?
DEFENDANT:	I said what the hell has that got to do with being a machine operator?
PROSECUTOR:	Can't understand a word. Can you, my Lord?
JUDGE:	Not a word. Am I supposed to take this applicant seriously?
PROSECUTOR:	Well, we shall have to get an interpreter. Anybody here speak spastic?
INTERPRETER: (Elane)	Yes, My Lord. I have an impressive range of degrees in foreign languages, including several dialects in spastic.
PROSECUTOR:	Thank God for that. Well, you ask it how fast it can type.
INTERPRETER:	(*In spastic imitation*) How fast do you type?
DEFENDANT:	I applied for this job because it doesn't require typing.
PROSECUTOR:	What does he say?
INTERPRETER:	He says that he applied for this job because it would not require typing.
JUDGE:	Answer the question. That's no answer.
DEFENDANT:	At eleven words a minute, but so what?
INTERPRETER:	He says at eleven words a minute, but he still doesn't see the point of the question.
PROSECUTOR:	Eleven words a minute. Not exactly lightning. Why is it so slow?
DEFENDANT:	Because I use a stick attached to my head.
INTERPRETER:	Because he uses a stick attached to his head.
JUDGE:	A what? A stick? Is this some kind of joke? What does he take me for?
PROSECUTOR:	What about making coffee?
DEFENDANT:	What the hell has that to do with machine operating?
INTERPRETER:	He says what the hell has that to do with

	being a machine operator?
PROSECUTOR:	Listen, we'll ask the questions here. So what's the answer?
DEFENDANT:	I'd drop it.
INTERPRETER:	He says that he'd drop it.
	(*Pros. and judge exchange meaningful glances.*)
PROSECUTOR:	How about reaching filing cabinets above his head?
DEFENDANT:	That would be difficult if I couldn't reach them.
INTERPRETER:	He says that would be rather difficult if he couldn't reach them.
JUDGE:	And what about getting into the front door, eh? There's a step.
DEFENDANT:	A ramp would be helpful.
INTERPRETER:	A ramp would be helpful.
JUDGE:	A ramp! Does he think I am made of money?
PROSECUTOR:	The prosecution rests, My Lord. It is our contention that the defendant is completely unsuitable for this job in spite of his educational achievements, as he fulfils none of the criteria of competence required.
JUDGE:	Thank you very much. Has the defendant anything to say before we pass sentence?
DEFENDANT:	You can take this job and stick it up your arse.
JUDGE:	What did he say?
INTERPRETER:	Ur ... he said thank you for considering his application.
JUDGE:	Quite so. Well, you've heard what the prosecution has to say. And very impressive it is too. In the opinion of this court, the defendant should be taken from this place and put in a sheltered workshop and there detained at the state's pleasure.

DEFENDANT:	Not a sheltered workshop.
JUDGE:	You will feel more at home amongst your own kind and you will find the work appropriately rewarding.

(The cast form a row – as in a sheltered workshop. They chant:)

1–2–3–4–5–6
In out, in out, in out
Here we are making baskets
In out, in out, in out
Here we are making baskets
In out, in out, in out
For £4 a week
In out, in out, in out
For £4 a week
In out, in out, in out
Isn't it fun making baskets for £4 a week
In out, in out, in out
Isn't it fun making baskets for £4 a week
NO!

c) *Feedback*

There was some reaction and laughter. In particular, the line 'up your arse' provoked a cheer. Jag started the discussion.

Jag:	People are very ignorant of the disabled. People tend to ignore me.
Questioner:	You must have had some qualification for the job as machine operator?
Jag:	I went to a special training centre. [There were other questions of a similarly literal nature.]
Nic:	Has anybody had similar experiences?
Answer 1:	Yes. It was very true to life. People spoke to me as if I was deaf or stupid. I still get that every year.
Answer 2:	When they're filling in a form for you. They talk to the form and not you.

Answer 3:   You get employed for a few weeks or
                 months, but if they can't make up the
                 numbers at Remploy you're paid off. I
                 don't know how they judge a person. You
                 can't learn a job in eight weeks. [Remploy
                 is the government-supported sheltered
                 employment. To be employed by them
                 usually requires certain competencies and
                 work rates.]

The discussion was somewhat low-key and disjointed
compared to others elsewhere. Comments tended to be
anecdotal and at times irrelevant. Slightly disappointed by
this, Nic split the twenty-eight people into three groups. He
suggested the theme of relationship between the helper and the
helped or the teacher and the taught.

d) *The Workshop*

Group 1 was taken by Elane and Ellen. They gathered in a
circle at one end of the hall and started by exchanging names.
There then ensued a general discussion of Graeae, how the
company came about, what Graeae means (see p. 169), what
the play *Sideshow* was about and how the company works. This
was a diversionary tactic to stop anything actually happening,
so the leaders had to bring it to an end and draw the
participants back to what they should be doing. There was
general apathy about the next move and nothing emerged. At
this stage one person actually left the group and wandered
round. The leaders initiated an activity whereby people had to
decide what they would most like to learn. They then
attempted to pair them up so that some teaching activity could
be explored. Eventually after considerable delay and
discussion three sub-groups emerged. One was going to look at
a driving lesson, another was investigating a typing lesson and
the third, a skiing class. There was a lot of activity and noise as
they prepared their pieces.

Group 2 was led by Yvonne, as Deniz had a migraine and
went to lie down after performing the sketch. The group

started with a general talk about the International Year of Disabled People (IYDP). Yvonne quickly organised a therapist to sit next to each disabled person. She then encouraged them to converse in pairs, talked to each pair about what they were doing, and made suggestions. Most pairs were going for role reversal, so Yvonne could ask questions such as, 'What disability are you dealing with?' Occasionally she generated some sort of heightened response by asking questions like, 'What makes you angry?' There was not much general activity or movement. At times one got the impression that particular pairs were passive and non-communicative.

Group 3 was taken by Nic and Jag. They sat round in a circle making suggestions. There were various ideas about being 'left out' and about a 'teaching class where the teacher gets it wrong'. Gradually the group evolved into a conversation about the relationship between a disabled person and a helper. Each participant had a story to tell, so Nic structured it so that first of all the disabled people could say what they really disliked, and then all the therapists could follow suit. At one point one of the disabled people exclaimed that he really resented being told what he could and could not read. Apparently there had been a *cause célèbre* involving a local sex bookshop that had been closed. 'Why can't I read a sex magazine in this town? Why do I have to read the Bible?' is how he put it. A heated exchange occurred between a therapist and her disabled client on patronising attitudes shown towards a wheelchair dance team which she ran. The group was totally static but the concentration was intense.

e) *The performance*
Group 3 went first, and as they had not actually worked on a sketch they decided to encapsulate their workshop in a one-sentence statement from each member on what they most disliked. (Most statements identify whether the speaker is able-bodied or not.)

Speaker 1:   What I dislike is when in company and they're handing out tea, if I'm with an able-bodied person they don't ask me, they always ask the person next to me.

Speaker 2:   I went to see an elderly client who wanted me to put sugar in her tea. She was perfectly capable of doing it, but I did it to avoid a conflict.

Speaker 3:   At a sports competition, I didn't mind when they helped disabled people in the early rounds of pool. But I did in the final.

Speaker 4:   I have this feeling of being used. I assess a client and make an appointment to call back with the equipment. But they want me to make an appointment when it's suitable for them and not me.

Speaker 5:   When I use public transport, I wish they would let me alone. I can get on and off by myself.

Speaker 6:   When I go to a pub a barman often refuses to serve me because he thinks I'm drunk.

Speaker 7:   When people find out you're disabled they ignore you.

Speaker 8:   I dislike it when people say they're coming to visit me and they don't.

Speaker 9:   I got no support from disabled people to bring Graeae up here. I feel the disabled don't put in the same as I do.

Speaker 10:   I dislike the word 'special'.

Group 1 was the next to go. The first of their sub-groups had decided to perform a driving lesson. There were three student OTs who were the pupils and the instructor, who was disabled. They followed him around on chairs while he gave them instructions. The humour was more of a sexist nature as the OTs were female and the instructor male. In fact the punch line was 'bloody women drivers'. The second sub-group had two elderly ladies re-creating a typing lesson. In an extremely simple set of repetitive exercises the two women evoked a quiet and charming relationship. The third sub-group had an element of farce in that a woman with cerebral palsy took a group of therapists for skiing practice. The effect was

READY SALTED CRIPS, 1974
Performed by students of Hereward College of Further Education, Coventry

Above: *Left to right:* Philip Rider, Hazel Peasley, Gill Slow. Photo: Richard Tomlinson

Below Left: Gill Slow and Nabil Shaban. Photo: Richard Tomlinson

Below Right: *Left to right:* Gill Slow, David Maxwell, Hazel Peasley. Photo: Richard Tomlinson

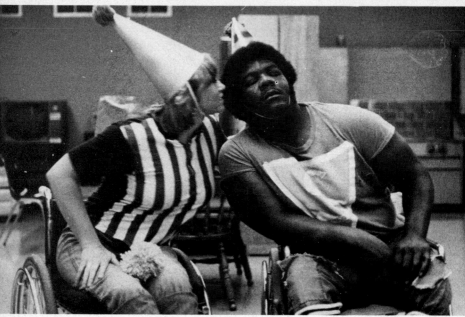

Top: 'Come and See the Freaks.' *Left to right* Gary Patti, Barbara Merdins, Glen Hebert, Bob Trotter. Photo: F. D. Maglione

Centre: 'Beauty and the Beast.' Rhonda Jub and Bob Trotter. Photo: F. D. Maglione

Bottom: 'The Strong Man.' Bob Trotter. Photo: F. D. Maglione

SIDESHOW, 1980–81
Performances by the Graeae Theatre Company in theatres throughout Britain

Top: 'Will's Accident.' *Left to right:* Marion Saunders, Alex Low, Will Kennen. Performance at the Riverside Studios, Hammersmith, January 1981. Photo: Brian Astbury

Centre: 'Witchdoctor.' *Left to right:* Marion Saunders, Jag Plah, Will Kennen. First London performance, Summer 1980. Photo: Brian Astbury

Bottom: 'The strangest and weirdest freaks.' *Left to right:* Mike Flower, Nabil Shaban, Deniz Bulli. First performance after Graeae had become a full-time, professional company, Summer, 1981, Photo: B. J. Warner

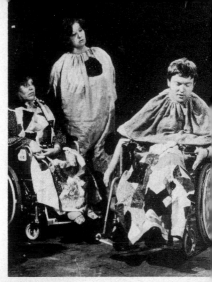

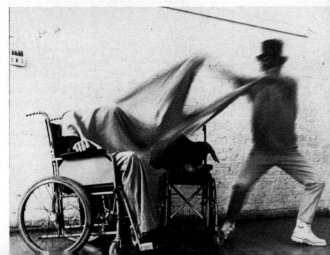

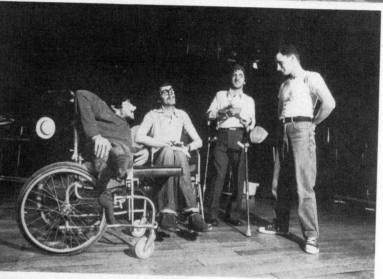

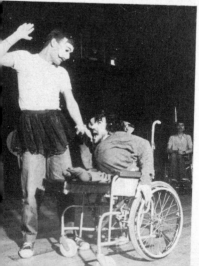

Top: 'The Miss Crippled Universe Sponsor.' *Left to right:* Mike Flower, Nabil Shaban, Jag Plah, Deniz Bulli. Photo: Bob Chase

Centre: 'The IYDP Committee.' *Left to right:* Nabil Shaban, Mike Flower, Jag Plah, Deniz Bulli. Photo: Bob Chase

Bottom: 'Beauty and the Beast.' Deniz Bulli and Nabil Shaban. Photo: Bob Chase

Top: 'Freak Chant.' Jag Plah and Nabil Shaban. Photo: Bob Chase

Centre: 'The Bank Raid.' *Left to right:* Ellen Wilkie, Jag Plah, Deniz Bulli. Photo: Ingrid Gavshon

Bottom: 'The PM exhorts employers not to employ the handicapped.' *Left to right:* Ellen Wilkie, Elane Roberts, Yvonne Allen, Jag Plah, Deniz Bulli. Photo: Ingrid Gavshon

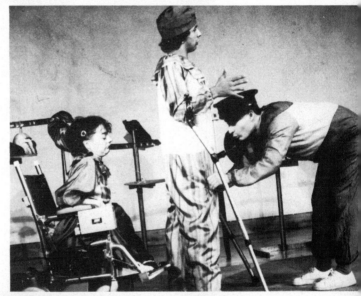

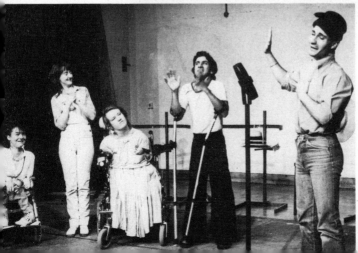

WORKSHOP

Given by students at Beaumont College for Physically Handicapped School Leavers, Lancaster

Photos: courtesy of Beaumont College

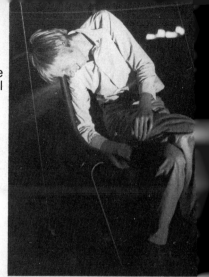

A benefit book for Karny. Yvonne Allen and Deniz Bulli. Photo: Richard Coward

Yelda at Karny's squat. Yvonne Allen and Elane Roberts. Photo: Richard Coward

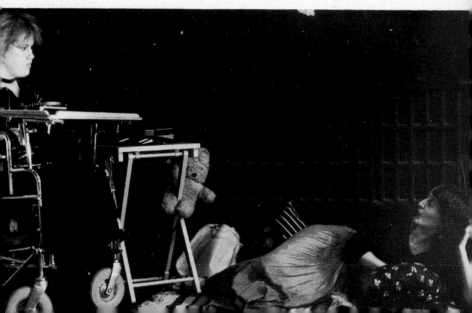

Top: Outside Richard's office. *Left to right:* Yvonne Allen, Ellen Wilkie, Elane Roberts. Photo: Richard Coward

Centre: The 'M3 Junction 4' Song. *Left to right:* Yvonne Allen, Deniz Bulli, Ellen Wilkie. Photo: Richard Coward

Bottom: Nic Fine, Director of the Graeae Theatre Company. Photo: Ingrid Gavshon

ludicrously funny.

Group 2 performed a series of role reversal sketches. All were based on the reactions of the disabled client (therapist) to the ministrations of the therapist (disabled person). The way each viewed the other was not only enlightening but extremely funny. One was an attempt to get the 'patient' to feed herself. The 'therapist' was totally believable and much enjoyed re-creating a situation in which she had often been on the receiving end. Another had an 'OT' visiting an 'old lady' with a stroke. Again the humour was in the immediate recognition of a familiar situation. Underlying it, as with the other sketches, was a deep mistrust in the relationship between client and therapist.

f) *Conclusion*

The abiding memory of this workshop is that it only touched on the complicated and delicate relationship between the therapist and the client. Group 3 had stated it explicitly. Group 2 displayed it in humorous sketches. The clients felt patronised and the therapists, used – scarcely a good relationship. In discussion afterwards it was agreed that drama was one of the few channels which could explore this relationship in a constructive way. The problem, of course, was that this initial exploration was not going to be developed. The workshop was a one-off. Sadly, the possibility of this work continuing with this group of people is remote.

It was also interesting to discuss with the company how they thought it had gone. I observed that Nic, the director, had taken the lead throughout. He argued that this was not of his making, but that the company foisted this role on him. He was going to take steps to make sure that the introductory talk would be shared amongst all the company.

The tone of each group was very different, but all had achieved the stated aim of producing something at the end of the two hours. The quality of the offering varied from entertaining but slightly trivial games, as with Group 1, to profound and quite weighty statements from Group 3. But everybody had contributed. Many of the individual sketches had been led by disabled people. By so doing they had elevated their status to that of initiator of action instead of passive recipient of services.

5: The Evolution of a Play

This chapter concentrates on Graeae's working methods in evolving a new piece. I shall take the latest production (at the time of writing) and go through the various steps that led to the finished product. In the next chapter there is a full script, for reference.

The Needs
Having made the commitment to develop our own work, Graeae then had to come up with an idea of what the next show should be. There were certain constraints and needs. *Sideshow* had been performed over two hundred times and was beginning to look a little tired, as well as boring for the performers. The next show, *3D*, was a very theatrical piece needing, ideally, a theatre and stage lighting for maximum effect. It was not a good show for touring and playing the varied types of audiences that Graeae can expect to meet. What was needed was a robust, vital, tourable show that was accessible to all and could be played anywhere. It was to be a replacement for *Sideshow*.

To be tourable the show had to have a minimum of set and a style that would not require a complicated lighting plot, or indeed any lighting at all. Ideally it should offer five parts of roughly equal worth, so that the company would be used to the full. These were the physical realities and constraints. We had yet to decide what the play should be about.

Initial Ideas
The process of coming up with a new piece was helped by an

arrangement we had made with an independent television company to make a pilot film for the fourth channel, in the hope that funds would be forthcoming for three programmes. It was decided that this pilot should be on how Graeae decide what show to do, and how they set about doing it. That sort of pressure concentrates the mind wonderfully, but it also imposes an unfamiliar environment: however hard one focuses on the matter in hand, one is still aware of the prying eye of the camera and of the technicians flicking in and out of vision. The presence of a TV crew also exacerbates the tensions that are inevitable in the initial discussions.

None of us arrived on the first day of rehearsal and filming with any firm ideas as to how to proceed or what to aim for. Early on, however, we decided not to do a 'set up' job just for the cameras. We would go about it as if a film crew was not there. If, at the end of the week, we had got nowhere, then that was as valid for a 'fly on the wall' type of documentary as if we had come with clear, concrete proposals.

The first discussions showed one thing clearly: that everybody disagreed as to what should be attempted. Some wanted to do a straight play, others wanted a new type of *Sideshow* revue, others had no clear idea. Various suggestions were tossed out. 'Why not do a send up on IYDP?' was one. This was pursued to the extent of collecting information on the various disasters that had occurred so that they would be counterpointed with the generally positive publicity accorded the year by the media.

Grim stories of cut benefits, of social-services red tape, of services closed, were gathered. But the one story that generated considerable discussion and heat was the Dr Arthur case. Dr Arthur was a paediatrician in Leeds who was brought to trial for allegedly allowing a severely handicapped baby to die. He was acquitted, but the verdict was controversial in many quarters. The company felt this was well worth exploring. Doctors, parents, social workers, the general public, had all expressed views. The potential victim never had the chance to comment. Graeae, who has in its midst people who might well have been at considerable risk at some stage in their lives, could offer that perspective. Yvonne, who had been seriously handicapped as a result of thalidomide, had strongly stated views. How could she not argue against such behaviour, for was it not denying her own right to live?

This point was put in another context by another person, who was deaf. She had inherited this condition and knew it was extremely likely that she would pass it on to her children. This caused her considerable anguish. However, she concluded that not to have children, even though the likelihood of their acquiring deafness was high, was again a denial of her own right to live. If her children were to grow up deaf, what could be better than having a deaf mother?

The issues raised by the Arthur case are complex and of great moral importance, and Graeae is perhaps the only theatre company that can explore them with authority. But it was decided that, attractive as this idea was, it was not ideal because it did not fulfil the criteria as outlined at the start of this chapter. We were still looking for a *Sideshow* replacement.

The next idea to offer hope as a tourable, accessible, funny show was to do a real-life Punch and Judy show. The format is colourful and the characters entertaining. Moreover in one of the early seventeenth-century scripts there are characters such as the blind man and the blackamoor, which solved some casting problems. Stereotypes abound, not least of all Mr Punch, a hunchback and the epitome of the amoral, disabled court jester. This theme would allow an exploration of the tradition of associating disability of the body with an evil mind. Literature is well stocked with these characters – from Richard III, through Long John Silver, Captain Hook and so on. The difficulty was to tie these various ideas into a consistent theme that would fit nicely into a Punch and Judy format. It was not easy, and in the end had to be abandoned, although, I hope, not for ever.

We were back where we started. In proper Graeae manner we decided to ask each member of the acting company individually what he or she wanted to do. Then out of their comments we might be able to discern a common thread that could be developed into a show. The TV crew were excited at the possibility of doing this on film. We played on this more searching interview technique by priming two members of the TV company to ask the questions.

The opening question was, 'Why are you a member of Graeae?' followed by questions such as 'What sort of theatre do you think Graeae should do?' and 'Do you have a responsibility to explore the theme of handicap in a theatrical form?' Again the answers were confused, and at times flatly contradicted each other. Most did not want to do shows about disability, but still felt a deep anger about the way they, as disabled people, had been treated. Most said they would not have worked for a company like Graeae if they had had the opportunity to join a more conventional company. Only one felt that Graeae had a distinct political role in representing disabled people's experiences and views. Most just wanted an opportunity to act. In short, the company's collective view did not seem to coincide with the aims of Graeae that I have outlined earlier. Out of this confusion the director, Nic, and I had to find some pattern. The discussion ranged round the differences and the discrepancies, and the one area that did seem to suggest a common experience was that of limited choice.

All the members of the company had joined for their own personal reasons, but as disabled people they had been severely restricted in choice, and, as one of them put it, 'It was either Graeae or nothing.' This subject seemed to offer an approach that allowed for the varying aspirations of the company while providing some sort of theme. So we planned to set up an improvisation that would explore choice. We had to think of a parallel situation whereby people were given the choice of pursuing a certain line of action or suffering the consequences. The parallel that suggested itself was that of the private citizen who, in times of national emergency, could be conscripted to join the army to defend the country against an aggressor. The individual is given an extremely limited choice. He either joins the armed forces, or he is treated as a conscientious objector and suffers the consequences. In other words, he does have a choice, but he has to be very committed to opt for the anti-social and unpopular one.

Social attitudes towards disabled people are not unlike a government's attitude to all fit men in times of national emergency. Both attitudes ignore the individual differences and adopt a blanket description. Thus all people who have some sort of physical impairment are lumped together as 'the disabled', just as all active men over eighteen are 'the conscripted'.

Having established the rationale, we then had to consider the format of the improvisation. We decided to impose upon this collection of individuals a series of government measures that would force them to recognise a group identity and respond as a cohesive political force. So we made up various laws for disabled people, involving the issue of passbooks, the restriction of mobility and accommodation, job reservation, and finally a restriction on whom they would marry or have physical relations with. As Nic is from South Africa and I had some experience of that country, it was natural to look to its apartheid legislation as a model. We found that the tone often adopted by South African ministers in discussing their dealings with the black and coloured communities was very similar to that used by politicians in this country when referring to the disabled. Paternalism and condescension are the common attitudes. We felt that any government could impose extremely restrictive measures against disabled people, in the honest belief that they were doing the right and most helpful thing.

We then had to see how this would affect each member of the company. To further the conflict we planned to withdraw one member before the improvisation and brief him or her on what we, now in the character of left-wing agitators, feared the government was planning (although nobody as yet had any confirmation of it). We would then encourage that individual to warn the others and attempt some sort of group response.

So with this as our master plan we first of all withdrew Elane to brief her on the forthcoming government proposals. Elane was chosen quite deliberately as she had expressed most political commitment in interview. She was certainly the most politically involved of the group and was a natural choice for any left-wing organisation to contact. We advised her that if she was able to establish some cohesion and political drive in the group, then they would receive all the support that left-wing organisations could muster. We further warned her that this was just a start in the government's oppression of minority groups. Blacks, gays, and so on were also to suffer under even tougher measures. The disabled were to be the first simply because they had no political identity and no political clout. We left her to divulge this to the others in her own way, and we asked the individual members of the company to react to Elane as they would if she started talking about this topic in the course of a usual day. We also introduced various signals which would indicate a TV or radio announcement or would allow us to withdraw Elane for further briefing.

Predictably the company's initial reaction to Elane's observation was one of disbelief and boredom. There was certainly no interest in reacting to what at that stage were only rumours. TV broadcasts announcing the introduction of passbooks for all disabled people also failed to evince any communal reaction. All the while Elane was plugging away, encouraged by the left-wing agitators, at establishing some sort of group identity and some sort of organisation. She informed them that there was a meeting about the implications of these measures, that everyone should go to. Again there was a considerable lack of enthusiasm. Indeed Deniz aggressively rejected any such suggestion. The discord between Elane and Deniz was becoming a shouting match.

Then Nic and I decided to introduce the black passbooks, and so we pulled individuals out of the group improvisation to be confronted by us, as representatives of the government, asking questions and issuing books. Ellen quite happily accepted her book and gave information about her accommodation and her job. Yvonne was far more hostile. Jag refused to cooperate and would not move. Nic and I subjected him to pretty aggressive questioning about his lifestyle, his earnings, his methods of transport and so on. Jag refused to reply and was getting more and more upset. Just at that moment the dispute between Elane and Deniz got completely out of hand and Deniz pushed her to the floor. Elane reacted by pushing back and then burst into tears. Nic and I rushed in to separate them. Everybody was stunned, including the film crew who, fortunately as we thought, had not actually filmed the incident.

At that time the incident assumed catastrophic proportion. Elane was racked with sobs, Deniz was distraught and rigid with tension, the rest of the company were shocked and frightened. It seemed to me that we faced the real possibility of the company breaking up there and then. Fortunately they are made of sterner stuff. But at the time it was a real fear.

Incidents such as these teach us lessons. Nic and I were the first to accept the responsibility for letting the improvisation get out of hand. We were very aware that the actors themselves did not have the experience to know when to withdraw from a situation that was in danger of becoming a physical confrontation. It meant that in all future improvisations we would have to impose strict rules so that the individual was protected. The difficulties posed when reality intrudes upon improvisation to produce violence obviously had to be discussed. However, the immediate problem was how to get the show back on the road. We suggested doing something entirely different, and we settled on playing various games with a forced heartiness that only just managed to conceal the feelings of fear and vulnerability experienced by all the company. Of course, we had to get down to discussing the incident and seeing what we could get out of it – including whether it could be used to the benefit of the play. We could not ignore what had happened, but if we were going to talk about it, it had to be in a positive way; otherwise mutual recrimination would only exacerbate the already tense situation.

A common denominator quickly emerged. The fact of physical handicap made all the participants that much more vulnerable to physical assault. We asked Ellen why she didn't intervene. She replied, 'What could I do? I'm in a wheelchair.'

She had no strength. Yvonne, similarly, could do nothing physical to intervene. Elane felt extremely vulnerable as she could not see her aggressor. One of her fears, as expressed in *3D*, was of physical violence. Deniz, had also, in the same play, spoken of the increased danger of assault because of his inability to be visually forewarned. So this company, more than a physically able company, was traumatised by violence. This partly explains their unwillingness and inability to band together to fight aggressive government measures. As long as it did not affect them personally they were not prepared to take action.

This led naturally to discussions on the responses of other identifiable groups to repression. The reaction of German Jews to Hitler's Germany was a case in point. We discussed the stage at which individuals are prepared to accept a common denominator so that they can protect themselves. We found the disabled to be in a very strange position. To fight for his individual rights, a disabled person has to relinquish his most cherished desire – that is, to be seen as just another member of society. It is conventional to condemn the labelling or lumping together of disabled people. And yet the only way to fight for rights and against discrimination is to accept this label and try to organise an effective political lobby.

The discussion thus came back to the starting point of the improvisation. It is hardly an acceptable way of conducting such an exercise, but the very fact of physical assault had crystallised the whole problem that we had set out to explore. So out of a very unfortunate incident there were some benefits, but the fear that pushing an actor to his limits might produce similar results could jeopardise future improvisations. Only a rigid application of the 'if you get too upset walk away' rule and the experience of successful improvisations would obviate that.

This incident occurred half-way through the week's filming. We planned to have a small scene written, rehearsed and performable for the final day's shooting. I was able to script three scenes that came directly out of the workshop but were much lighter in tone, which helped ease the atmosphere greatly. The first scene was a TV announcement by the Minister for the Disabled on the issue of black passbooks – benefit books to all disabled people so that 'needs could be identified and met'. The second scene was discussion following this broadcast between Ellen and Elane, the latter seeing it with ominous foreboding and the former with optimism. The final scene was Deniz as a social services volunteer visiting a bemused Jag Plah to give him a black benefit book. Apart from Elane's warning, there was no attempt to convey any sense of threat or oppression.

The scenes went reasonably well, and indeed had an element of humour in them. At the end of the week we felt we had a possible show that would be far more political than the previous ones but would still allow the actors to develop their skills.

Characterisation

One of the most repeated wishes of the company was to be given the opportunity to develop characters on stage. They felt that *Sideshow* was a series of lampooned caricatures and that *3D* was an extension of themselves. They all wanted to 'act' in a more conventional sense. Given the situation as outlined above, it was perfectly possible for each actor to devise his or her own character. The main proviso, of course, was that they could not pretend they did not have the handicap that they actually had; or if they did hide it, they had to have a good reason. Each actor was asked to prepare a dossier on his character.

Yvonne chose Karny Jones. She was an only child: father a bank clerk, mother a secretary with an insurance company. She was born in Bath but moved to London where she attended a comprehensive school. Truancy and petty thieving, and mixing with the 'wrong sort', led her into trouble with the police. She now squats in a flat in London with her mates and is the singer in a rock group, 'Insipid Puke'.

Jag was Rajah Singh, known as Roger. Came over from India when a child. Started business with a barrow in Petticoat Lane. Graduated to shops in Southall and now a club in the

West End. Aged twenty-eight. Lives extremely well; will only go out with white girls. Sails very close to the wind legally.

Deniz was Richard David Jamieson. A civil servant living in Wimbledon. Married with two children. A very suburban member of suburbia. Father a senior civil servant worried about mortgage repayments. Would like a bigger car. Travels to Waterloo daily. Has been having an affair with secretary. Likes gardening. Under no circumstances does he admit to partial sightedness.

Ellen was Lizzie Baxter, a feminist and political writer. Married to Robert with whom she was at university. Has a baby girl, Freya. Very into causes – CND, women's rights, Brixton (had a West Indian boyfriend for a while). Doesn't get much published. Reads the *Guardian*.

Elane became Yelda Sinclair. Father a high court judge in Scotland. Attended a special school for the blind. Hated it. Has always been interested in men. At fifteen met a middle-aged man who seduced her and introduced her to pornography. Expelled from school and disowned by parents. Started sleeping around, got kicked out by lover. Does a little modelling and when hard up, a little call-girling.

All members of the cast, apart perhaps from Yvonne, were deliberately playing against themselves and some, especially Elane, had overdrawn their character. However, I felt that all these characters were so diverse that when the blanket legislation on disability appeared they would all react in very different ways. I thought that Karny would reject it out of hand; Roger would exploit it for his own ends; Richard would be implementing the measures in constant fear of exposure; Lizzie would be duped at the start into being all in favour of legislation; Yelda would drift through it all, playing by her own rules.

Plot

The bare bones of a plot had been introduced in the first improvisations, but in the meantime various ideas had emerged. It was important to bring the characters together so that dialogue could advance the action. If they were all in isolation there would have to be a series of monologues or a heavy reliance on the telephone. Getting the characters all together fitted in quite well with the idea of disabled homelands (a parallel with black homelands in South Africa). We were also encouraged by the announcement in the press that, as a result of IYDP, five Arab countries were contriving to create a city for the disabled. Communities exclusively for disabled people are nothing new: Het Dorp, a village in Holland, has been running for some time. So we would have to pack off all the characters to some settlement exclusively for the disabled.

But we had to find a good reason for that, because it would obviously be expensive. The solution was in the unemployment figures. If all disabled workers were taken from their jobs and put in a settlement with sheltered employment, something like half a million jobs would be available for the able-bodied. Likewise, if a policy of repatriation were pursued, unemployment would be solved overnight. We considered that there were elements within the conventional political parties who would welcome both these moves, and that we could incorporate both elements into the play. We also felt that the spirit of paternalism that motivated most public utterances on disabled people (in particular we thought of the Queen's 1981 Christmas speech) implied that a resettlement plan would be universally supported.

We then had to decide where we would establish communities that could amount to three to four million people. Again inspiration struck when working around our home base in Aldershot. Aldershot is the home of the British Army. It is full of barracks, garages and hangars – ideal for disabled people. So all we had to do was get rid of the Army from Aldershot, Catterick and the other barracks. Ireland was the natural contender for military occupation. In a once-and-for-all attempt to solve the Irish problem, there was to be a saturation of troops policy.

So a scenario started to emerge. The first half of the show could be an explantion of why disabled people were being herded together in Aldershot. The second could be a description of life in a camp where people's personal liberties and choices are being slowly eroded. The climax could be their reaction to this.

The second part of the plot was reminiscent of *Sideshow*, in which the members of a freak show had sought to escape from the ministrations of institutionalised life. This new play was emerging as a sequel, and we were tempted to call it *Uncle Sidney Strikes Back*. But the recollection of *Sideshow* gave us the idea of how the inmates could escape. They would form a theatre group and tour other settlements as well as able-bodied towns, exposing the corruption and oppression of the disabled townships. The model, again, was black theatre that had come out of South Africa, fiercely hostile to the regime. Plays such as *Sizwi Bansi is Dead*, *Boesman and Lena* and *The Island*, all by Athol Fugard, were a source of inspiration. Most recently the play *Woza Albert*, which told of Christ's second coming to South Africa, showed how theatre could be used to condemn, in brilliant, witty performance, the injustices of apartheid.

There are a couple more twists to this particular approach. First, such a plot would lampoon Graeae itself. We were set up with very similar aims. Secondly, political theatre does not necessarily prick the bubble of complacency and paternalism in an audience. Black South African theatre, although revolutionary in intent, does get shown, and, indeed, is sometimes sponsored by the government. Fostering a group that is ostensibly biting the hand that feeds it actually has the effect of removing the teeth. So revolutionary theatre has not resulted in revolution. It could be argued that it has allowed the South African government to display a liberal and progressive attitude in censorship which is totally out of keeping with its other laws. Moreover, it can turn round and say, 'You call us repressive, and yet not only do we allow radical whites to publish their work, we even offer them sponsorship.'

Inevitably one gets the feeling that political work brings no dramatic changes: it is a slow war of attrition. And for the inmates of Aldershot, it is the same story. No matter how revolutionary and critical their material is, they will still receive the bland approval reserved for any activities of the disabled, coupled with the pitying comments, 'Of course they're bitter. Wouldn't you be bitter if you were like them? It's very understandable..., etc.'

So the climax of the piece could be the shattering – by the establishment's approval and support of their efforts – of the group's belief that they have struck a blow for liberty and the extension of choice. This would be very much a reflection of Graeae's own feelings after a particularly ineffectual performance.

Content

We now had to put the characters and the plot together, and see what happened. It quickly emerged that Richard Jamieson was a crucial character. He could become the instrument of government policy, which would allow much more interchange in the first half. Richard, as a civil servant, could be responsible for contacting the other characters, issuing them with black passbooks and seeing them off to Aldershot. His own personal crisis would come when it was discovered that he, too, was disabled, and he would be sent to Aldershot as the senior administrator. His exposure to the rest of the group would precipitate a breakdown.

The other characters began to develop. Roger Singh quickly becomes a comical crook always on the fiddle, always just one step ahead of the law. He could be caught attempting to quit the country under a false identity, to escape a tax case. He would then be offered the job of transport coordinator in Aldershot, on the grounds that no one had fiddled the 'motability' scheme as successfully as he.

Lizzie Baxter, as the typical liberal progressive joiner of worthy causes, embraces anything from single parent families, to prostitution reform legislation and the Society for One-Legged Lesbian Dwarfs. As such she is just the person to carry the banner for disabled rights, and naive enough to believe that Aldershot would provide just the forum. Her encounters with Roger Singh would open her eyes to the behaviour of some disabled entrepreneurial types.

Yelda becomes far more of a wanderer, a free spirit. More by accident than design, she escapes Jamieson's attempts to track her down. It is typical of Yelda that she arrives at Aldershot by mistake, having hitch-hiked down the wrong motorway. However, she is a survivor and has a strong ability to manipulate people to get what she wants. She winds Roger Singh round her finger, just as she chats up the guards on the gate to get in and out as she wishes.

Foul-mouthed and anti-social, Karny is perhaps the most honest character. From the start she knows intuitively that Aldershot will mean increasing discrimination and repression. She is the most let down when a final blow for freedom in the form of a protest song fails because the audience patronises her.

We started giving the characters situations. Karny visits Roger to try and get a record published. He's not interested. Richard interviews Lizzie and finds a potential ally and confidant. Yelda dosses down at Karny's squat. Roger gets waylaid by Richard at Heathrow *en route* to Mexico. The first half inevitably relies, to a certain extent, on coincidence and contrived meetings. Everybody uses the telephone to advance the plot.

But the real problem at this stage was how to introduce information about government legislation. In improvisation we had just shouted announcements, but now we had to find some theatrical convention. We experimented with TV screens and radio announcements. But in the end the temptation to send up the Establishment was too great, and so I wrote in scenes that dealt with Cabinet meetings, discussions between the Ministers for Disability and Employment, and the Queen's 1981 Christmas speech. As I mentioned earlier, that speech, with its emphasis on the courage of disabled people, had been greeted with some derision by the company. The word 'courage' became increasingly part of the language of contempt that the inmates of Aldershot employed. Thus the Courage Arts Centre was the theatre where the Courage Players would be performing. Aldershot was formally renamed Happiness Valley.

There was the technical problem of how the Establishment figures should be portrayed. They had to be sufficiently detached from the real action to appear as cardboard cut-outs. We debated this for some time, and in the end came down in favour of using large puppets. We felt they would be theatrically exciting and would bring colour and drama to venues that did not have lights or any form of staging. The actors would have to operate the heads and provide the voices. We also had to have a narrator to set the scene, particularly at the start. We found that playing scenes very fast one after another, in different locations, with an actor playing maybe more than one part, necessitated some form of commentary.

So the first half became a series of short scenes establishing characters, however crudely, and outlining the plot as clearly as possible. The second half could afford to allow far more interaction and a deeper exploration of the individual characters. Roger Singh could evolve from a laughable spiv into a rather scary senior official and bully-boy at Happiness Valley. Richard, having been a pompous official, could reveal a more human and warm side. Lizzie could see her own folly in the light of incontrovertible proof of the corruption and dishonesty of the officials. Yelda could appear slightly colder and more calculating than the dreamy sexpot of the first half. And even Karny could articulate political convictions that in the first half were expressed in obscenity. The scenes could become longer and, hopefully, all the characters more real. Only the Establishment would maintain their aloof and ludicrous views.

The second half, more than the first half, was based on the improvisation of specific confrontations. Richard, as the resettlement officer at Aldershot, encounters Yelda who is 'on her way through' without a black passbook. The ensuing improvisation became an hilarious verbal seduction of Richard, leaving him totally bemused and out of his sexual depth. This was my one opportunity to base the script on this improvised encounter. And Richard's admission to Lizzie, in confidence, that he too is a holder of a black book, allows an exploration of Lizzie's outrage at his weakness and deceit that helped enormously in precipitating his breakdown.

Roger as the wheeler-dealer has a marvellous opportunity to explain to Lizzie why he is selling inferior goods at superior prices to the inhabitants of the Valley. As he explains, he can only bring in goods at night because all his drivers are Indians and Pakistanis who are superstitious of the place. 'But what can you do? These Indians and Pakistanis have no education.' Only Jag could have come up with a line like that. Yet it was totally in character for Roger Singh. Karny can show herself in her real colours when, having reviled Richard all through the play, she is the first to attempt to get him off drugs and back to some semblance of normality.

All these insights came out of improvisation and contributed enormously to the richness of the characters. Once the structure was established, the development of the characters was much easier. Relationships could be examined, and actors' reactions to situations explored. Individual lines were often culled from improvisation. And, even if lines or reactions jarred, here was an opportunity to discuss and analyse character so that nobody was bound by a poor line to adopt a motivation that was inappropriate or irrational. Improvisation is a marvellous source of ideas and, indeed, of individual speeches. It is much easier to edit the raw material and rewrite it than to create characters and lines straight out of one's head. It also gives the actors, as well as the writer and director, the opportunity to be in at the birth of the character. And when in due course the character has taken on a life of its own, other actors can imbue it with their own vitality.

Conclusion

The proof of any theatrical pudding is in the performance. At the time of writing, *M3 Junction 4* has not been performed. At the time of reading, it will have been performed many times. That experience will have brought about refinement, development and change. A new company will interpret the characters in their own way. It is their misfortune not to have been present at the conception, gestation and birth. They will have to go through a different process to 'find' the part.

After its traumatic beginnings, this play proved very easy to write because everything fell into place quickly and after a minimum amount of disagreement. One of the last decisions to be reached was that of the title: suggestions included *Passbook*, *Aldershot's the Spot*, *Handiland*, *Goldfish Bowl*, and *Exit to Aldershot*. That last gives the clue to the final title. Junction 4 is the turn-off from the M3 that you take to get to Aldershot.

6: M3 Junction 4
(or Happiness Valley)

Characters
Announcer
Queen
Minister for the Disabled (Hugh)
Minister for Employment (Norm)
Prime Minister
Lizzie Baxter – a committed journalist
Roger Singh – a crook
Yelda Sinclair – a drifter
Richard Jamieson – a civil servant
Karny Jones – a rock singer

} puppets

Act I

ANNOUNCER: Good evening, Ladies and Gentlemen. To start with we have a special honour. We are able to catch the final few words of Her Majesty's Christmas broadcast, so we will go directly over to Buckingham Palace.

QUEEN: Courage has many forms, be it the police in trying circumstances in Brixton, the Army in Northern Ireland, the bomb disposal experts in our own capital city or the disabled who perhaps personify the individual courage that we can admire and from which we can take inspiration. And now, at this festive time of the year, we can look back at the people who have contributed to this year with gratitude and admiration for their patience, forbearance and, above all, their courage.

ANNOUNCER: The Minister for the Disabled has formally brought the International Year of Disabled People to an end with the message that the lessons learnt this year and the initiatives made must not be allowed to lapse.

MINISTER: It has been a source of great encouragement to my office to see the amount of work and activity done on behalf of disabled people. Why, in many activities disabled people have themselves taken a full and equal part...

ANNOUNCER: Meanwhile at No. 10 Downing Street, the Government has other concerns.

PRIME MINISTER: (*Chairing a Cabinet meeting.*) ...the projection for long-term unemployment could scarcely be called encouraging. Any thoughts on the matter, Norm?

NORM: Er... I would suggest, ma'am, that ... er ... maybe the Chancellor should consider injecting a little money into the economy to create some...

PM: Norm, you're wet.

NORM: But there is an election, and we have to do something if we're going to win it. Four million unemployed is not exactly election-winning.

PM: Norm, I do suggest you think of something. And pretty quickly, if you don't want to be written into the history books as the Minister for Unemployment. You have two weeks to come up with something, and Norm, it had better be good. (*Exit.*)

NORM: Oh hell, what can I do? I mean there aren't the jobs there.

(*Enter* MINISTER FOR DISABLED.)

MIN. FOR
DISABLED (HUGH): Hello Norm, how's it going?

NORM: Oh hell, Hugh, she's on the warpath. I've got to come up with something on unemployment in two weeks. What am I to do?

HUGH: Resign, old boy. Lumber the old cow.

NORM: Hugh, how can you? It's all very well for you. You came out of last year smelling of roses. Lot of positive publicity on the disabled, lowered the benefits, closed a few training centres, two Acts that'll cost us no money. I mean you're laughing. What would you do in my place?

HUGH: Give me your salary and I'll tell you.

NORM: Oh, Hugh, please don't take the Michael.

HUGH: Wash your mouth out.

NORM: Sorry. You see the sort of state I'm in?

HUGH: ... Look, there are thousands of people who are in jobs who are incompetent.

NORM: Yes, just look around.

HUGH: Now, no names, no pack drill. But consider if we had all the incompetent people unemployed, and all the competent people employed.

NORM: Fat chance. The unions would create merry hell. I mean the Monk tried to weed out bad teachers. No chance.

HUGH: You need to hit a section of the community who can't hit back.

NORM: Well the coons are out, then. That's all the bastards do. Hit back.

HUGH: And they're all out of work anyway.

NORM: What about the Micks?

HUGH: Wouldn't mind having a go at them, but you can scarcely stop people in the street and ask them for a sample of their accent.

NORM: Well, who then?

(*Fade.*)

ANNOUNCER: After these deliberations, let's hear some comments from the man in the street.

(*Fade.*)

LIZZIE: Who the bloody sodding hell has nicked my typewriter ribbon (*screams*)? Robert, you bastard, have you been messing about with my typewriter again?

(*Fade.*)

ROGER: (*Leans back and pours himself a scotch.*) Listen, I'll tell you how I got started. Borrowed a barrow off a mate and started flogging Indian cultural items made in Southall.

(*Fade*)

YELDA: (*On phone.*) Oh, darling, how nice of you to call. What? Well not just at the moment, darling, I'm a little occupied, but maybe in about half an hour? Till then. Bye, darling.

(*Fade*)

KARNY: (*Writing song and singing it to herself*)

The smoke gets up your nostrils

It gets into your eye

I need to lie in bed

Unless the baby cries

I haven't any feeling

For me or us or them

It's all the same

Every day

And the smoke still

Goes straight up.

Oh God, that's rubbish.
(*Enter RICHARD, dressed in coat and hat,*

carrying briefcase.)

RICHARD: (*Removes and hangs up coat and hat. Turns over polished name plate. It reads:*

RICHARD JAMIESON
WELFARE OFFICER
SOCIAL SERVICES

The telephone rings and he answers.)
Yes sir. Right away sir. (*Exit.*)

LIZZIE: ... and the next time you go to the shop, for Christ's sake remember we need matches (*hits keyboard, talking as she types*) ... 'The neo-imperialist regime, as in the case of the Reagan administration's involvement in Guatemala, is totally rejected by...'
(*Fade.*)

ROGER: (*On phone.*) OK. So you can do with four dozen at £3 a unit. All right, all right. No, I promise, not a word. Yes, I'll see you're all right. Don't worry, my friend. I'll be in touch.

KARNY: Oh, Mr Singh?

ROGER: Yes.

KARNY: I had an appointment.

ROGER: Yes.

KARNY: Miss Jones, Karny Jones.

ROGER: Yes.

KARNY: You know, the rock group an' all? Insipid Puke?

ROGER: Oh yes. Come in. Now I run certain sorts of establishments – sophisticated, I like to think.

KARNY: Well I brought a demo tape, see. And a recorder. How about havin' a little listen? All right then? (*Switches on. Song –* KARNY *mimes along.*) What you think, eh? Different init?

ROGER: Oh yes, it's that all right. Now, Miss...

KARNY: Call me Karny.

ROGER: Well, Miss Karny, I really think . . .

KARNY: I'm real sorry the rest of the group couldn't
            come. I mean you'd love 'em. You see it's
            really important that women recognise their
            right to play a central role in the smashing of
            mass-circulated recording rubbish. I mean it
            is, isn't it? Total bleeding garbage. Now
            there's Wack on bass, Colly on drums,
            Razor on keyboards, Perry on percussion
            and Twang on rhythm. Shit on lead – we call
            her that 'cos she's shit hot, and I do vocals,
            see. My mate is Razor, she reckons I'm a
            smart bleeder, well once a month anyway –
            get it, get it, eh? So that's it. Insipid Puke.
            Great name.

ROGER: Miss Karny, I am a busy man. I really think
            we are wasting each other's time to go on.
            I'm afraid this is not the sort of music my
            clients would appreciate, meaningful and
            significant as I'm sure it is. I'm sorry, but
            that's an end to it.

KARNY: Oh. Well, all right, me old immigrant mate,
            we'll just have to hawk it around elsewhere.
            Ta. See you then. You'll be kicking yourself
            in a couple of years.

ROGER: I'll risk it. (*Exit* KARNY.) I think I'll stick to
            Sari selling. (*Takes a swig of whisky.*)
                          (*Fade.*)

YELDA: (*Packing.*) Oh well, here we go again. (*To her
            teddy*) On the road again. All men are
            bastards. (*Sits down and looks through address
            book.*) Now let's see. Mmm. Looks as
            though it'll have to be Geoff in Brighton.
            Could never stand the smell of his feet, but
            beggars can't be . . . Hey ho. (*Picks up
            phone.*) Blast, the swines have cut off the
            phone. Oh well, Ted, it looks like rule of
            thumb to Brighton. And you never know

your luck. Remember the company director in the Mercedes? That was an exhausting weekend. But fun. Getting sick of this grotty place anyway. (*Opens case.*) Shan't miss this, or him, at all. (*Exit.*)

RICHARD: (*Enters with file. He opens it, stares closely, looks round carefully, then takes out monocular aid and examines the document very carefully. After a bit, he sits back and looks ahead.*) Christ. (*Picks up phone.*) Dad, I think I might have a problem. Well, there's this file. Oh, you know about it. Yes, and what about me? I mean, oh, thank God for that. Don't worry, I'll keep it well hidden. You'd better believe it.

(*Fade. Enter* PM *and* NORM.)

PM: Ah, Norm, a word in your ear. I do like the proposals on unemployment.

NORM: Thank you, ma'am.

PM: But if we take all the troops out of Aldershot, will it not cost a lot of money to convert the barracks?

NORM: Well, ma'am, according to our figures, if all disabled people are taken away from their present jobs then that will give us 500,000 jobs to fill and will cut unemployment accordingly.

PM: So there are savings in social security?

NORM: Precisely.

PM: And the centralising of resources at places like Aldershot will be economic?

NORM: Oh indeed yes, ma'am.

PM: And, of course, the chiefs of the Armed Forces are delighted at the prospect of action. Now tell us, Norm, this is but a start?

NORM: Oh yes, ma'am. We are going ahead with repatriation schemes, to the West Indies,

	Pakistan, India and Southern Ireland. That would give another three million.
PM:	Marvellous. At a stroke we have saved unemployment, united public opinion against the IRA, and provided improved services for the disabled, entirely in keeping with the sentiments of last year. Well, now, I think I've solved it.
NORM:	May I humbly suggest, ma'am, that it was my idea?
PM:	I think this calls for a major speech now. I think I can hail it as a stroke of genius.
NORM:	Thank you, ma'am.
PM:	Not you, you fool, me.
NORM:	Of course ma'am, exactly ma'am.

(Fade.)

ANNOUNCER:	The Government, in a major initiative to solve the Northern Ireland situation, has adopted a saturation of troops policy. In the next few weeks, battalions at present based at Aldershot, Catterick and RAF Lyneham are to be transferred to Ulster, in a final bid to wipe out the influence of the IRA. The Minister for Northern Ireland has expressed the view that this new hard-line attitude has considerable support in the province. Protestant leaders have expressed enthusiasm for the move, and even Catholic spokesmen have spoken of it as offering a 'once-and-for-all' solution.
LIZZIE:	(*Opens a letter.*) Oh, shit. Another rejection slip. I really think nobody takes feminism seriously. Robert, you haven't done the washing up, and there's the bloody ironing as well. I'm going out to the National Childbirth Society meeting, so for Christ's sake put the baby to bed at seven. No later. All right? Bye.

ROGER: (*On the phone.*) Look, I'm sure we can reach some sort of agreement. Yes, yes, I know the returns for 78–79 are missing at the moment. No, that's right. I wasn't in the country; my associate of the time, Mr Pandit Singh, was handling affairs. Yes, that's right. He was repatriated in 1979, as an illegal immigrant. I can only assume he took the books with him. You do see my problem, don't you? You want me to come in with the books and ledgers? Of course. I'll look forward to seeing you. Wednesday? Of course. (*Puts down phone.*) Oh hell, where's my passport? (*Pulls out three or four.*) Now, who should it be this time? I think Ingmar Johansen, Swedish exporter, is out. Winston N'Gomo, professional wrestler, I don't think so. Ah – here we are. Floyd McNamara the Third, from Dallas, Texas. (*Opens drawer in desk and removes stetson – affects a Texan drawl.*) That should sure fool the critters. (*Pulls out a pair of high-heeled boots and takes off his own shoes – getting boots on is a major struggle – he gets up with crutches and staggers round with them.*)

(*Fade.*)

RICHARD: (*Has a list which he is going through intently. The phone rings – he picks it up.*) Hello. Social Services Welfare Section (*snaps to metaphorical attention*). Oh yes, sir. Yes, it's all in hand. Yes, sir. I have the list. Yes, sir, it was made clear that South London was my responsibility and I will be putting into immediate effect the survey and the issue of black passbooks. Sorry sir, I meant benefit books. I understand. I, of course, will be watching the ministerial broadcast this evening with considerable interest.

(Fade.)

ANNOUNCER: The Government's initiative of a massive injection of funds for disabled people has come as a major surprise in today's budget from the Chancellor. The opposition has added its support to the measures and a spokesman is quoted as saying that it would be mean-minded to criticise such a wholesale change of heart by the Government, only adding the comment, 'What took them so long?' At a press conference this evening, a spokesman from the Department of Health and Social Security outlined some of the details.

SPOKESMAN: This must be seen as a red letter day for the disabled. This Government is now pledged to full employment and adequate housing for all registered disabled people. In a move to sponsor positive discrimination, a survey is to be put into immediate effect so that the real needs of disabled people can be assessed and analysed. On the basis of these findings the Chancellor has assured the Cabinet that funds are available to mount the necessary programme to meet the need. These moves are a direct result of the closest communication between the Disabled Department and leaders of the disabled community. Disabled people will be issued with a benefit book to guarantee them maximum support from programmes. Please don't lose your book. It is the passport to a fuller and better life.

(Fade.)

RICHARD: *(On phone.)* Mrs Baxter?
LIZZIE: Yes.
RICHARD: This is the Social Services Welfare Department. May I ask you a few questions?

	It's in connection with the Government's new policy on the disabled.
LIZZIE:	God, that's quick. But about time, if I may say so. I've been campaigning for years for disabled people's rights. You may remember my letter to the *Guardian* on this matter, last November?
RICHARD:	Er ... er... Yes, Mrs Baxter. It was actually about you that I just wanted to clarify a few matters. Could I perhaps pop round for a few moments a bit later?
LIZZIE:	Of course. But not today. Let me see, this evening it's the Friends of the Earth, tomorrow it's up to London, demonstrating with CND, and then Friday we've got the working party on Save the Whales, and then it's the weekend. Oh God, it's the weekend course on One-Legged Lesbian Dwarfs. It'll have to be next week. Say Tuesday – all right?
RICHARD:	(*Dazed.*) Of course, Mrs Baxter. Goodbye. (*Next phone call.*) Is that Miss Jones?
KARNY:	Who wants to know, squire?
RICHARD:	It's the Social Services.
KARNY:	What do you bastards want? I assure you I have not been claiming dole and working. You bastards are so nosey.
RICHARD:	No, no, Miss Jones. I assure you it's nothing to do with dole. It's . . .
KARNY:	Oh yeah, that's how you sneaky pigs try and get round us, ain't it? What's it about then? Attendance allowance, mobility allowance? What you trying to take away from us this time? Anyway, how the bloody hell did you know where I was, I'm not usually here?
RICHARD:	Well Miss Jones, this is the telephone number I have for you. Where do you normally reside?

KARNY: Ha! Wouldn't you like to know? Anyway, it's got no bloody phone, so you're out of luck, sunbeam.

RICHARD: I do assure you, Miss Jones, it is an effort to assist you. It's in connection with the new benefit books, you know, the Government policy document. I really am trying to be helpful.

KARNY: Helpful my arse. You just want to put me on your bleeding computer. Well, stick it, sweetheart.

RICHARD: But, Miss Jones... (*She hangs up.*) Oh dear. (*He tries another number.*) Line out of order. This is a bit harder than they anticipated. (*Hat and coat on – exit.*)

(*Fade.*)

YELDA: (*At a bar.*) Well, darling, I just do a little modelling on the side, you know. But it's really such a bore, I much prefer travelling and talking. Well thank you. I think just a teeny campari and soda. Lovely. And how about you? Please tell me the story of your life. Absolutely, from moment A. (*Drinks, interjects* 'marvellous', 'lovely', *but is getting progressively more bored. Finishes drink.*) Well, darling, I really must be going. Fresh air in my hair, don't you know. Oh, have you? Well, a little weekend in East Grinstead is exactly what I could do with. (*Gushing now.*) That sounds simply terrif. Let's have one for the road shall we?

(*Fade.*)

(ROGER *staggers in still in stetson, cowboy boots, carrying case as if for airport. Mutters foreign mutterings to himself.*)

RICHARD: (*Steps up to him.*) Aah, Mr Singh.

ROGER: What, me? No, no. Ma name is Floyd McNamara the Third, Junior, from Dallas,

	Texas, the biggest and widest state in the Union.
RICHARD:	Quite so, Mr Singh. There are just a few questions I'd like to ask.
ROGER:	Why, holy cow. Ah'm a citizen of the United States of America and I will not be harrassed by tinpot officialdom.
RICHARD:	I do like your boots, Mr Singh, but I'm afraid you'll have to delay your flight to Mexico just a little while. You will be aware of the new Government measures on behalf of the disabled. You must be very excited at the boost this'll give your business.
ROGER:	What are you talking about? I'm not disabled.
RICHARD:	No, Mr Singh? You are collecting constant attendance allowance for three people; you run a fleet of taxis on the motability scheme; you have tax concessions for eight dependants. I think that would classify you as disabled, Mr Singh?
ROGER:	Well, er, I'm sure there's some mistake. Take me to ma ambassador. Ah claim diplomatic immunity.
RICHARD:	No, no, Mr Singh. You've got it all wrong. Your sort of initiative and endeavour is exactly what the Government is looking for, Mr Singh. You are the acceptable face of disability. You're hardworking, competitive and full of initiative. I mean, running a fleet of taxis on motability – it's brilliant.
ROGER:	Well, it was quite easy really.
RICHARD:	So, Mr Singh, we really don't want to lose your special little skills to some foreign land, do we?
ROGER:	Well, I'm not so sure. I mean (*recovering himself*) Ah'm Floyd McNamara the Third, Junior, from Dallas.

RICHARD: Now, Mr Singh, you will have your joke, but I'm sure you wouldn't want any more questions about your tax returns for 1978–79, would you?

ROGER: Oh.

RICHARD: This way Mr Singh.

(*Fade.*)

LIZZIE: (*Holding black passbook – painting slogan.*) At last, real friends for disabled people. God, this is marvellous. It really shows that if you push and keep pushing, then you can really get somewhere. I did hear that at the Women's Body Rights Society meeting the other night, they were talking about me as the disabled world's Emmeline Pankhurst. Wow! That's some compliment. And now, with this (*waves passbook*), I must put my energies into developing disabled consciousness. We must unite and continue the fight for disabled rights. (*Holds up placard.*)

DISABLED PEOPLE
FIGHT FOR RIGHTS
PEACEFULLY

(*Fade.*)

RICHARD: Oh, Miss Jones, I've come to deliver your benefit book.

KARNY: Why do I want this grotty book, eh? Look, matey, I don't want the bleedin' welfare state, nor bleedin' nosey parkers like you. Don't you realise we're all victims of capitalist fascism? You're just a lackey. Give it all up now, before it's too late. Come and join us in the squat. It's life; it's freedom.

RICHARD: Look, Miss Jones, this book gets you help. You do need help, don't you?

KARNY: I've got me mates. Razor helps me. I don't

	need your help. As long as I've got them I'm all right.
RICHARD:	But will you always have them? What if you get left here? It's up three flights of steps. You might need help then.
KARNY:	They won't leave me. What are you talking about? They're my mates.
RICHARD:	Well, I hope you're right. But, just in case, keep hold of your benefit book. All right? (*Exit.*)
KARNY:	I don't need no benefit book. (*Hurls it down.*) ANARCHY RULES!

(*Fade.*)

| ANNOUNCER: | The Minister for the Disabled today commented on the issue of black benefit books. |
| MIN. FOR DISABLED: | ... I am delighted at the enthusiastic response from disabled people everywhere to the census and the issue of benefit books. The development of information storage and retrieval systems within Central Government has allowed us to analyse and quantify need in considerable detail. On the basis of this I am able to outline our first programme which is to provide adapted housing in specific areas. Social services officers have been instructed to advise disabled clients on the availability of new accommodation. In some instances, this may require a change in location, but housing is available now. Some people have expressed reservations at the issue of the black benefit books. I can reassure you categorically that these are for your benefit – to cut red tape – to expedite services. Please use them. They are your passport to assistance. |

(*Fade.*)

| ANNOUNCER: | Troops are now settling into their new |

homes in Belfast with their customary good humour. Ulstermen have welcomed the military influx with enthusiasm and traditional Ulster hospitality. It is now proposed that the deserted barracks in Aldershot and Catterick will not be allowed to fall into disuse, but are being adapted as special holiday camps for the disabled. Work is already under way, widening doorways and building adapted bathrooms, and the first parties of disabled people are expected to arrive soon.

(Fade.)

RICHARD: Well, we seem to be getting somewhere at last. Now, who have we left? Mmm – yes, there's that woman Sinclair. Yelda Sinclair. I wonder where she can have got to.

(Fade.)

YELDA: *(Arrives at Karny's squat.)* Hello. Anyone here?

KARNY: Who's that?

YELDA: Ah, thank God for that. It's me. Well we sort of don't know each other, but a friend of a friend, I think she calls herself Blade or some such – no, no it was Razor – said that if ever I was fearfully up against it, then I could always have a piece of floor.

KARNY: Oh, you're a friend of Razor's are you?

YELDA: Well, more of an acquaintance. I think it was at that show at Hyde Park that we had a little chat.

KARNY: God, you're blind.

YELDA: Well, yes, darling. That's absolutely true.

KARNY: How did you find your way here?

YELDA: I do have a tongue, so I grip some lovely man in a scrum outside the tube station and tap my way along.

KARNY: Blimey. Well you'd better come in. There's

not much room, but I think there's a mattress in that room.

YELDA: One thing, sweetie. I seem to catch the roar of some strangely fangled machine. Are you on something I don't know about?

KARNY: Probably. I'm in an electric wheelchair.

YELDA: Well, well. Birds of a feather. Why are you in that? I mean it's up three flights of stairs.

KARNY: Come and shake hands and you'll see.

YELDA: What darling little hands. Don't you ever get out?

KARNY: What, outside? Yeah, course I do. My mate Razor humps me up and down the stairs. Just haven't seen her for a couple of days.

YELDA: Well, should I make the tea or will you?

KARNY: Haven't got none.

YELDA: Something slightly harder?

KARNY: No.

YELDA: Food?

KARNY: No, I told you, Razor's not been here.

YELDA: You poor pet, you must be famished.

KARNY: Don't think about food really.

YELDA: Mmm. A teeny bit of embarrassment, but have you got any money? I'm just a fraction broke until I get some from my ex.

KARNY: Oh, yeah. I got money. Here, how much?

YELDA: Oh divine. I'll get some goodies and be back in a jiff. Promise.

KARNY: (*As* YELDA *goes.*) Yeah. You won't be long, eh? (*Exit* YELDA.) Hope she doesn't nick it.
                         (*Fade.*)

RICHARD: (*Labouring late over files.*) Sinclair, Sinclair. I've tried everything. The hospitals, the police, supplementary benefit. She must be on the road, or shacked up with some man. Blast. It's spoiling the graph. North East London are doing better. I need those extra increments. God, we could even get a washing machine.

(*Telephone rings.*) Hello. Social Services Welfare Department. Yes, Richard Jamieson speaking. Oh yes. He's what? Oh God. My father, you mean? No. When? I mean, how is he? A heart attack? Oh God. I'll be round. Which hospital? St Mary's, right. I'll be round straight away. (*Phone down, head in hands, slowly takes eyeball and puts it into his pocket.*) Oh God, what now? (*Exit.*)

(*Fade.*)

(KARNY *and* YELDA *are having a meal.*)

YELDA: (*Brings in the food.*) Here we are, then.

KARNY: Gawd, that's better. For a blindy, you can't half cook. How do you manage?

YELDA: Trial and error, my dear. Trial and error. When did you last eat, Karny?

KARNY: Oh, a day or so ago, you know.

YELDA: Is it all right if I stay a few days?

KARNY: If you cook like this, too bleedin' welcome. Hey, you bein' blind and that, you've got a black book ain't you?

YELDA: A what, darling?

KARNY: A black book. A so-called bleedin' benefit book. Look. (*Hands hers over.*)

YELDA: No, dear. What are they?

KARNY: Haven't you been pestered by the Social Services giving you books and all? I mean, it's all over the TV, the radio and the papers.

YELDA: I seem to have been rather occupied of late. So do give me the lurid details.

(*Fade.*)

(LIZZIE *comes into the waiting room of* RICHARD'S *office. She sits and waits, drums her fingers, takes out a letter and reads it again.* ROGER *enters. Takes a seat. Grunts. Sits down.*) (*Pause.*)

LIZZIE:	You waiting to see Jamieson?
ROGER:	Uh? Er, I have a letter from Mr Jamieson.
LIZZIE:	I like your boots.
ROGER:	They're killing me.
LIZZIE:	Oh, why do you wear them then?
ROGER:	I like them.
LIZZIE:	Oh. What do you do then?
ROGER:	Bit of this and that. You know, dealing in a variety of commodities.
LIZZIE:	I'm a writer.
ROGER:	Oh, very interesting. Do you do advertising copy?
LIZZIE:	I feel that advertising is a form of prostitution, don't you?
ROGER:	Prostitution? No, I didn't mean that sort of advertising. But you wouldn't be involved in that sort of business, would you?
LIZZIE:	What do you mean? I do take an interest in prostitution reform legislation. But I think we have our wires slightly crossed.
ROGER:	Do we? I don't see any wires.
RICHARD:	(*Rises from desk and moves to* ROGER.) Mr Singh. We have already met, of course. Do come in. (ROGER *sits in front of* RICHARD's *desk.*) Now, I do apologise for the rather brusque way I spoke at the airport. The thing is, Mr Singh, I have an offer to make you.
ROGER:	An offer?
RICHARD:	Yes. As you know, the Government is putting out for tender several very large contracts connected with the redevelopment of army barracks at Aldershot for holiday homes for the disabled.
ROGER:	Is it?
RICHARD:	Surely you've seen the news items connected with the budget?
ROGER:	Oh yes.

RICHARD: Well, the thing is, Mr Singh, the Government is particularly interested in encouraging disabled people to take the initiative in these matters, so that jobs can be found.

ROGER: What do you mean? I'm not really disabled. I have a bit of a limp.

RICHARD: But Mr Singh, you have grasped the intricacies of the law concerned with disabled people, in a way that I have never seen matched. Your spotting and exploiting the various loopholes is nonpareil.

ROGER: None what?

RICHARD: Without compare.

ROGER: Without what?

RICHARD: It's very good.

ROGER: Oh, yes.

RICHARD: Now, I have it on very good authority that the Government would view extremely sympathetically any bid for a contract say, on transport, by a disabled person. Why, Mr Singh, you fit the bill.

ROGER: But, mmm, what will this mean to my various little financial difficulties at present?

RICHARD: Water under the bridge. Water under the bridge. Have a look at this file. There are of course several Government grants available for the right person. I think you'll find it most illuminating.

(Fade.)

(LIZZIE *in waiting room still.* KARNY *enters pushed by* YELDA.)

YELDA: These places are a mite intimidating, dear.

KARNY: Yeah. All the bastards want to do is rip you off. God, the number of files they must have on me. Got done for drink and driving when I was twelve.

YELDA: What were you driving?

KARNY: Me electric chair. Had half a bottle of British sherry and mowed down four pedestrians on the pavement, before hitting a milk float in the middle of a pedestrian crossing. There I was, covered in strawberry-flavoured yoghurt shouting, 'Who wants to win a stick of Chippenham rock'? The thing is they don't even make rock in Chippenham.

YELDA: Well, I think I'll go, dear.

KARNY: Not getting a black book then?

YELDA: Black's not really my colour, dear. A little morbid. I'm sure we'll bump into each other again, Karny. Love to Razor. Bye. (*Exit* YELDA.)

KARNY: Look after yourself. (*To* LIZZIE) Amazing woman that. Doesn't give a bugger about red tape at all. Amazing.

LIZZIE: (*Not interested.*) Mmm.

KARNY: You waiting for this Jamieson bloke too? Bloody nerve. They track you down and before you can get any more bread, you've got to roll up at the office clutching these bloody books.

LIZZIE: I think it's a major advance for disabled people.

KARNY: I don't give a stuff about cripples. I just want the bread.

LIZZIE: What do you mean, you don't give a stuff. You're one . . .

KARNY: What? One myself? I bleedin' am not. Wanderin' around in crocodiles, being patted on the head. I'm a rock singer, mate, not a cripple.

LIZZIE: I'm not trying to question your right to do what you want, but there are unquestionable physical realities.

KARNY: Stuff all your long words, mate. You can have your physical reality. I'll keep the music. (*Puts on cans.*)

RICHARD: We look forward to doing business with you, Mr Singh. (*Exit* ROGER.) Ah, Mrs Baxter. Sorry to keep you. Do come in. (LIZZIE *does so*.) Now, Mrs Baxter. I know you were very pleased at the Government initiative to improve services for disabled people. Now, as you know, the Minister wishes to encourage disabled people to take full responsibility for the development of programmes at Aldershot. Now, given your interest, commitment and track record in terms of publications, I had the temerity to mention your name to the Minister. I do hope you don't mind.

LIZZIE: No, no, not at all.

RICHARD: Oh, I am pleased. It is so difficult to find articulate, well read people who are activists and not just armchair philosophers – or should I say, wheelchair philosophers. Now I have a personal letter from the Minister, asking you for your assistance in this matter.

LIZZIE: A personal letter?

RICHARD: Oh yes, Mrs Baxter. The Minister made special reference to your letter to the *Guardian*. November, wasn't it? In the first instance he would welcome a briefing from you on the main objectives of the community in Aldershot. He would then be most grateful if you would supervise the arrival of the first groups and administer their allocation.

LIZZIE: This is very interesting, but I do have various domestic responsibilities.

RICHARD: Mrs Baxter. At present you are a freelance writer and your salary is unremarkable, not to say negligible. Your husband is a teacher, threatened with redundancy. I think you'll

	find the terms offered more than compensatory for the slight domestic disruption.
LIZZIE:	I'll need to look at the details and I'll have to talk it over with my husband.
RICHARD:	Of course, Mrs Baxter. Look forward to hearing from you. (*Exit* LIZZIE.)
	(*Fade.*)
KARNY:	(*Going through her benefit book tearing out page after page.*)
	He loves me.
	He loves me not.
	He loves me.
	He loves me not.
	He...
RICHARD:	(*Outraged*) Miss Jones.
KARNY:	Oh, Mr Jamieson. He loves me. And you never let on. Ain't that sweet?
RICHARD:	Miss Jones, that is Government property.
KARNY:	Well, they shouldn't have given it to me then.
RICHARD:	Miss Jones, that book determines your level of benefit.
KARNY:	Well, I can tell you now that I'm here, can't I?
RICHARD:	At present, you are living on the third floor of a terraced house, in a squat, right?
KARNY:	So?
RICHARD:	There is no heating or electricity and no lift.
KARNY:	So?
RICHARD:	You can't live like this, Miss Jones.
KARNY:	I can, and I am.
RICHARD:	But that's not living. I have found another place for you. Ground floor, accessible toilet.
KARNY:	But I'll stick with my friends.
RICHARD:	You'll be much more independent, Miss Jones. Warm, safe.

KARNY:	I'll stick with me friends.
RICHARD:	But will they stick with you?
KARNY:	What do you mean?
RICHARD:	Well, I believe that Insipid Puke – that is the name isn't it? – are actually performing in Aberdeen.
KARNY:	What? Course they ain't. I'm the lead singer.
RICHARD:	A poster, Miss Jones. And here is a letter from Razor, isn't it?
KARNY:	But . . . SHIT.
RICHARD:	The accommodation is extremely pleasant. I'm certain you'll have opportunities to write more music and indeed form groups.
KARNY:	SHIT.
RICHARD:	So, Miss Jones, we will provide the transport to Aldershot.
KARNY:	Oh, fuck off. I'm not going there. And this is what I think of your fucking benefit book. (*Rips it up and hurls it at him. Exit.*)
RICHARD:	(*On the telephone.*) Yes sir. Nearly 100 per cent. I think it's all organised. Yes sir. Why, thank you, sir. It was a terrible shock, but I'm coming to terms with it. Oh thank you sir. Goodbye sir. (*Puts phone down.*) What did he mean, best of luck in Aldershot? (*A sudden frenzied ripping open of envelopes. At last he pulls out a black book. Takes out his magnifier and examines it. It is what he fears. He puts the book into his breast pocket and his magnifier into a hip pocket.*)

Act II

(RICHARD's *new office. He enters as in Act I. The only difference is the name plaque – it now reads:* R. JAMIESON, COORDINATOR, RESETTLEMENT PROGRAMME. *He does not polish it with pride. Enter* ROGER – *he seats himself*.)

ROGER: Well, I thought I'd pop in to tell you how things are going, Richard.

RICHARD: Good to see you, Mr Singh.

ROGER: Call me Roger.

RICHARD: Roger. This really is a splendid opportunity for us all. I am most impressed by the transporting arrangements.

ROGER: Yes, the helicopter will be arriving shortly.

RICHARD: Helicopter?

ROGER: Oh yes. I thought we should do it with a bit of flair, this being a military base and all. I did want to parachute some spastics in, but they said they didn't want to end up paraplegic as well. But the world press is here. I'm sure they'll be wanting a statement from you.

RICHARD: Well, Mr Singh, Roger. This is most encouraging.

ROGER: Now tell me, after we've cleared this lot and I've sold the helicopter back to Sir Freddie, what are we to do about a little entertainment?

RICHARD: There is a recreation and entertainment committee.

ROGER: Yes, but they're only interested in rug-making and madrigal-singing. I mean entertainment. Get the turnstiles clicking. Know what I mean? Now, I dismissed legless high-jumping and spastic polo, but I think I've hit on a winner.

RICHARD: Really, Mr Singh, Roger?

ROGER: Yes – you know all those old invacars that have been withdrawn? Well, how about souping them up and having drag races? I mean they're very unstable, there will be lots of accidents. Thrills and spills in the Crip Car Rally – I can see it now. What do you think? Crowds will flock to that.

RICHARD: Mr Singh, Roger, I think we should be having a wider perspective and look at the cultural opportunities for developing theatre, opera, dance.

ROGER: Yeah, all right, some exotic dancing.

RICHARD: Mr Singh, Roger, not quite what I had in mind.

LIZZIE: (*Bursts in.*) Have you seen them? Sorry I didn't knock, Richard, but have you seen them?

RICHARD: That's all right, Lizzie, have I seen what?

LIZZIE: The helicopter arriving. It's fantastic – like the beach landings in Normandy. The helicopter touches down and ramps come down and out they roll – hundreds of wheelchairs. It's unbelievable.

ROGER: What did I say?

LIZZIE: Oh Roger, it's magnificent. And then they all took off, and everybody cheered. Will they be back?

ROGER: Oh yes, there are several sorties to be made. They'll be bringing people until nightfall, and again tomorrow. Then there is the bus fleet from Victoria station. And the special trains. I'm only sorry I couldn't get a couple of hovercraft up the River Alder, but there we go. You win a few, you lose a few.

RICHARD: So, Lizzie – how's things with you?

LIZZIE: I'm so excited I can hardly contain myself. At last it's really happening. The fight has got somewhere. But we mustn't become complacent.

RICHARD: No chance of that. I read your article in the *New Journal*.

LIZZIE: Do you like the title?

RICHARD: 'Into the Warm'? I think it says it all.

ROGER: There aren't very many pictures. I'm a Page

	3 man myself. Could we run a 'Miss Tits in a Wheelchair' contest?
LIZZIE:	Roger, that is the most chauvinist remark I've ever heard.
ROGER:	Sorry, just trying to be helpful.
RICHARD:	But I do take your point in the article about the need for cultural stimulation. Roger and I were just talking about it before you came in. You know, the Minister will be visiting in a few weeks' time. Must mention this to him. I'm sure he'd be interested in the cultural aspirations of disabled people.

(Fade.)

(KARNY *is sitting disconsolately in the street by a coffee bar.* YELDA *walks past.* KARNY *is flabbergasted to see her.*)

KARNY:	Yelda, Yelda! Is it you?
YELDA:	Why Karny, darling, of course it's me. What a surprise. What on earth are you doing here?
KARNY:	I've been dumped, like everybody else here.
YELDA:	Dumped? What do you mean?
KARNY:	You remember that time you took me to the Social Security office? Well the whole point of that was to get me out of the squat and down here.
YELDA:	But darling, that squat was simply awful.
KARNY:	That's not the bloody point. I wasn't given the option.
YELDA:	They just bundled you down here?
KARNY:	In a manner of speaking. I couldn't go back to the squat 'cos no one would help me up the stairs.
YELDA:	What about Razor?
KARNY:	Well, she's sort of not there.
YELDA:	Not there? What do you mean darling?
KARNY:	They've only gone and dumped me from the group and pissed off to Aberdeen.

YELDA: Oh, Karny, that's awful.

KARNY: Yeah.

YELDA: Well, you'll just have to start your own
            group here.

KARNY: Yeah, but Razor doing that! I mean she was
            me mate. Anyway what are you doing here?
            Jamieson's caught up with you. Got your
            black book?

YELDA: But, darling, where am I?

KARNY: Aldershot. Don't you know?

YELDA: Aldershot. Lots of lovely men in uniform. I
            thought I was just outside Brighton. So
            what's this, a sort of holiday camp?

KARNY: More like concentration camp. Don't you
            know nothing? Disabled people are being
            rounded up and put here. That's why you're
            here.

YELDA: It sounds a dreadful mistake. This sweet
            little man gave me a lift down the motorway,
            then turned off and said, 'Here we are!' I was
            a trifle surprised because it didn't feel like
            Brighton.

KARNY: You were on the wrong motorway, Yelda.

YELDA: Oh well. I shall just have to get on the right
            one tomorrow.

KARNY: Don't be daft, they won't let you out once
            you're here.

YELDA: Won't let me out? Karny, you are being a
            little fanciful.

KARNY: Yelda, you don't bloody realise. Once you're
            here, they'll nail you. Just like they nailed
            me.

YELDA: The man at the gate was awfully sweet and
            helpful.

KARNY: Oh, Yelda.

YELDA: Does that mean all the soldier boys in their
            pretty hats have gone?

KARNY: Yes – off to kick shit out of the Irish.

YELDA: I really think I need a drink. Do you have such a thing, sweetie?

KARNY: Oh, I got booze now, don't worry.

YELDA: Oh lovely, let's go and have a little drinky and I'm sure something will sort itself out.

KARNY: Got me own flat. No steps.

YELDA: Lovely.

(*Fade.*)

(RICHARD *and* LIZZIE *are in* RICHARD's *office.*)

RICHARD: Congratulations, Lizzie. I think your promotion is absolutely deserved.

LIZZIE: Thank you. I mean, it's a bit awesome to be Director of the Research Institute. But just think of the opportunities. I'm going to survey the whole population. There must be at least one book in it. Maybe two.

RICHARD: It's marvellous to see such enthusiasm.

LIZZIE: Oh, Richard, you've been so helpful. I don't know how I can ever repay you. It's been a privilege working with you.

RICHARD: Come now, Lizzie; you'll make me blush. I only wish that all the community were as cooperative and supportive as you. I've had several complaints from the older inhabitants about excessive noise and drunkenness. It really is too bad and very inconsiderate.

LIZZIE: I must say I always liked the idea of placing elderly people next to young ones. Gives that sort of family feeling, but I suppose it was bound to have its problems.

RICHARD: Well, I have to go and investigate one such problem now, I'm afraid. It's always rather distasteful.

LIZZIE: I'm sure you'll handle it with your customary tact.

RICHARD: Thank you, Lizzie. I do try.

(RICHARD *crosses to* KARNY's *flat. He knocks,*

KARNY *answers the door*.)

KARNY:	Oh, it's you. What do you want?
RICHARD:	May I come in?
KARNY:	No, you can keep out of my flat.
RICHARD:	I'm sure I don't have to remind you that this flat's the property of the Department of Resettlement and you are a tenant. Speaking of which, there are various conditions of tenancy which you seem to have broken.
KARNY:	Go on, go on. I've heard it all before.
RICHARD:	Complaints of excess noise late at night; record players turned up, singing, bottle-smashing, strange wheelchairs visiting at all hours, noxious smells, really the list is endless.
KARNY:	So what? What can you do, eh?
RICHARD:	Well, Miss Jones, I had hoped you weren't going to force me to say this, but I am empowered to levy certain restrictions, such as the denial of battery-charging facilities, and in the end I can authorise your transfer to the sanatorium as the most appropriate accommodation.
KARNY:	You wouldn't bleedin' well dare, you double-talking git. (*Enter* YELDA.)
YELDA:	Who is this darling man? (*Holds his hand. He is bewitched.*)
KARNY:	This is Richard bleedin' Jamieson. *Gauleiter* of *Stalag Luft* Aldershot.
YELDA:	Charmed. I'm Yelda Sinclair.
RICHARD:	Who?
KARNY:	Don't tell him your bloody name.
YELDA:	Yelda Sinclair.
RICHARD:	That rings a bell.
YELDA:	Does it, darling? What a lovely thing to say. Oh Mr Jamieson, you seem to have dropped something. Now do tell me what you're

	bothered about?
KARNY:	Tell him to piss off.
YELDA:	Something about noise? I'm awfully sorry, at times I just get carried away. You really mustn't blame darling Karny, it really is all my fault.
RICHARD:	Well er . . .
YELDA:	We're just trying to be hospitable, to inject a little colour and life into some poor dears' dejected state. Look on it as morale building.
RICHARD:	And as for the smell of strange substances burning?
YELDA:	But darling, the plumbing is a trifle bothersome, but please don't think I'm complaining, because we're awfully happy, aren't we, Karny?
KARNY:	No, I bleedin' am not.
YELDA:	You see you've upset her.
KARNY:	Yes, and now you can get out of this flat. Go on out, out, out. And don't come back.
RICHARD:	(*Being hustled out.*) Goodbye, Miss Sinclair. But do you live here?
YELDA:	Oh darling, just passing through.
RICHARD:	But . . . (*Exit.*)
YELDA:	Bye. (*To* KARNY) Darling, you shouldn't be so physical with the little man. He's really rather a darling.
KARNY:	He's a prat.

(*Fade.*)

(ROGER *is writing at his desk. Sign says:* CONTROLLER OF TRANSPORT-ATION. LIZZIE *knocks and enters.*)

ROGER:	Oh, hello, Lizzie. Come in.
LIZZIE:	This is rather a delicate matter, so I'll get right down to it. You know I've been conducting a survey for my book?
ROGER:	Oh yes. Excellent idea. I've been thinking

about titles. How about *Feminism is a Dwarf Issue*, or *Aldershot's the Spot*?

LIZZIE: I am serious, Mr Singh.

ROGER: Sorry – just trying to be helpful.

LIZZIE: In this survey, I have been interviewing people in their own homes, and I've noticed a great many Indian artefacts.

ROGER: Arty who? I don't think that's an Indian name.

LIZZIE: Artefacts – things – goods.

ROGER: Oh, little Indian souvenirs. Jolly good. They have been selling very well, very well.

LIZZIE: I noticed they are all chipped.

ROGER: Oh dear. I am sorry to hear that. Maybe people have dropped them. You know, some have not much grip, or bang them against their wheelchairs, or whatever. I am most sympathetic.

LIZZIE: No. They said they bought them in that condition, and as yours is the only shop that retails decorations for the home, they really don't have much choice.

ROGER: But Lizzie, I'm really not understanding this. I have received no complaints. None whatsoever. Everybody's happy, no?

LIZZIE: No. One couple said they'd complained, but all they got was abuse from your store manager.

ROGER: Oh, that's terrible. The man is a rascal. I will dismiss him immediately.

LIZZIE: And also, Mr Singh, the prices for these goods are very high.

ROGER: Lizzie, what can I do? The cost of transport. These items are genuine Indian, you know. They are not cheap. And there are my overheads.

LIZZIE: I have seen similar items, undamaged, in London for half the price.

ROGER: Similar, but not the same. But you know what the disabled are like. They always want something for nothing. Now I assure you, my profit margin is extremely thin on these items. Why, I scarcely cover my costs. Let me tell you something, in confidence, mind. All these goods have to be transported at night. At night. Because the drivers are scared of coming here. Can you imagine it? But these Indians and Pakistanis are not very well educated. What can you expect?

LIZZIE: Mr Singh, you have not answered any of my questions honestly. You slide out of everything.

ROGER: Now, Lizzie, can't we discuss this in more comfortable surroundings? How about coming to my place for a drink?

LIZZIE: It really isn't good enough. I'm taking this up with Richard.

ROGER: Tonight?

(*Exit* LIZZIE.)

(*Fade.*)

(KARNY'*s flat.* YELDA *is there.*)

KARNY: I hate it here.

YELDA: But, darling, you've got everything. Food, drink, wild parties. It's all been lovely.

KARNY: Yeah, and you've got your black book.

YELDA: Do you know, the darlings put it in braille too. I thought that was terribly considerate. It says: 'Yelda Sinclair – blind'. I don't think I've ever been called that before. Quite a novelty.

KARNY: Yeah, but you're here now.

YELDA: I shall have to pop down to Brighton some time. Geoffrey is absolutely panting. But I really don't want to leave you all downcast.

KARNY: But, Yelda, it hasn't got into your head. You are here now. You've got a black passbook.

They won't let you out.

YELDA: How do you know? Have you tried?

KARNY: I can't. Jamieson's threatened to take away my battery-charger if I cause any more trouble.

YELDA: I went to see the little man on the gate. And he was terribly helpful. I really don't think he'll be a nuisance, and the poor dear seemed so grateful.

KARNY: Oh Christ, Yelda. I'm really choked. I've never been so bloody stamped on, even when I was in hospital. And Razor's dumping me. I mean, what can I do? I'm absolutely screwed. I will not go and work in one of those grotty factory units and have my benefit cut again. What am I going to do? I don't think I can go on.

YELDA: *Nil desperandum.* You must do what you want to do. I do.

KARNY: But you're different. I've never met anyone like you. You just drift through and get away with everything.

YELDA: No, dear. I decide what I want to do. If people don't want me to do it, I persuade them. It's really awfully practical. So what do you really want to do?

KARNY: I want to be a rock singer.

YELDA: Well, there we are then. Easy.

KARNY: It's not. Nobody likes my sort of music.

YELDA: But persuade them! Have you got any instruments and things?

KARNY: No – course I ain't.

YELDA: I'll go and see that charming Indian man. He's bound to have money.

KARNY: What, Roger Singh? He'll laugh in your face. I tried him when we were outside.

YELDA: Darling, leave it to me. I'm sure he'll be wild with enthusiasm.

KARNY:	God, Yelda, you're something else. I'm glad I've got you on my side. You are on my side, aren't you?
YELDA:	Darling, what do you think?

(Fade.)

(LIZZIE enters RICHARD's office.)

LIZZIE:	Richard, I really have to see you.
RICHARD:	Of course, Lizzie. I always have time for you.
LIZZIE:	It's Mr Singh. You've really got to do something.
RICHARD:	Mr Singh? Oh?
LIZZIE:	He's ripping off people left, right and centre. I challenged him over his Indian souvenirs, which I'm sure have never been near India, and he flannelled me about overheads and transport costs, and now I've just found out he's been telling someone that the water is polluted and he's been selling water from the tap, the same water, for 50p a bottle. It's outrageous. He's even charging parking fees for wheelchairs in toilets. You've got to do something.
RICHARD:	Now, Lizzie, don't get excited. I admire your integrity and honesty, but Mr Singh is a businessman, and I am sure is conducting his affairs very properly.
LIZZIE:	He's a crook.
RICHARD:	If you like, I will have a word with him. But it would be unfortunate to rock the boat just the week before the Minister's visit. As you know, he is actually going to rename the town. It's no longer going to be Aldershot. It's to be called 'Happiness Valley' – Mr Singh's idea, actually.
LIZZIE:	Richard, you are avoiding the issue. I don't care if the Minister is coming. Singh is a crook, and I shall take it up with the

Minister himself.

RICHARD: Oh, I don't think that would be very wise. I'm sure there are better ways of dealing with this. You see, the Government is very keen on private enterprise and fully supports Mr Singh. Why, it's saving them money, you see. I really don't think the Minister will be very receptive.

LIZZIE: God, Richard, you're wriggling about like Singh. Has he got something on you? What is it? The man should be exposed. You've employed a crook.

RICHARD: Well, I haven't employed him. It's the Department. But I will talk to him to ask him to curb his less agreeable sidelines.

LIZZIE: That's not good enough. You're the coordinator. You must do something.

RICHARD: I will, I will. Look Lizzie. I've always thought of us as friends, even confidants. Can I talk to you later, this afternoon some time?

LIZZIE: Why not now?

RICHARD: Well, it's rather personal, and it does have some bearing on the Singh business.

LIZZIE: Oh, very well. Five o'clock at my place. All right?

RICHARD: Oh, thank you. Yes, of course, Lizzie. I'll be there.

(Fade.)

(ROGER's *office*. YELDA *in full war paint knocks at door*.)

ROGER: Come in. (*On seeing* YELDA, *rises*.) Oh, come in, Miss . . .

YELDA: Yelda, darling, just Yelda.

ROGER: Oh, yes, Yelda. Can I get you something? A drink perhaps?

YELDA: A drink – that sounds like absolute nectar.

ROGER: It's only whisky.

YELDA: But a whisky's what I yearn for. Now, darling. Do show me where you've put the glass. I really can't fondle everything on your desk.

ROGER: Oh, I'm so sorry, of course. Here we are. Now what can I do for you?

YELDA: Mr Singh.

ROGER: Roger, please.

YELDA: What a lovely name, but I shall call you Rajah, so much more tropical, don't you think?

ROGER: That's my real name, actually.

YELDA: Rajah, there, I knew we would have a special understanding.

ROGER: Oh, I do hope so.

YELDA: Everywhere I go in town people talk about you, Rajah. What your plans are, how you've done this, done that. It's really quite remarkable that one man can have contributed so much.

ROGER: Oh, it's just work, you know.

YELDA: You must be so industrious – there's Singh's Food Markers, Singh's Drive-In Wheelchair Repairs, Singh's Take-Away Fish and Crips. It's never-ending. But then I noticed one teeny omission.

ROGER: You did?

YELDA: All great men, darling, I know, want to go down in history as benefactors of the Arts.

ROGER: They do?

YELDA: Of course – you just think of them all.

ROGER: Oh, yes of course.

YELDA: And I know that you would wish to be so remembered. You always think big, don't you? You want to build on the love and admiration that people have for you?

ROGER: Oh yes.

YELDA: So how about the Singh Centre for the

Performing Arts?

ROGER: The Singh Centre for Per... It sounds marvellous. But now, how about the Courage Centre for Performing Arts?

YELDA: You are so modest. Now here's a budget breakdown for a little place on the hill that absolutely fits the bill.

ROGER: £50,000? But, I can't, I mean ... £50,000?

YELDA: A man of your means – it's a trifle, and just think of the honour and respect. Why, Mr Singh, has there ever been a knighthood in your family?

ROGER: A knighthood?

YELDA: Sir Rajah Singh. When can we start?
(*Fade.*)
(RICHARD *crosses to* LIZZIE's *flat. Knocks.*)

LIZZIE: (*Coolly*) Come in.

RICHARD: Thank you for agreeing to see me, Lizzie.

LIZZIE: Would you care to pour the tea?

RICHARD: Of course, milk or lemon?

LIZZIE: I don't have lemon.

RICHARD: Of course not, so sorry.

LIZZIE: Now Richard, I'm still thinking of our conversation this morning, and I must say I still feel dazed. Singh is so obviously a crook, and yet you're defending him. Why?

RICHARD: I am not in quite so powerful a position as you think. That's why I wanted to talk to you privately, personally, as a friend.

LIZZIE: But he is a crook, isn't he?

RICHARD: I know his methods are at times a little outrageous. Look, what I'm trying to tell you, Lizzie, is very difficult for me. I've never told anyone else. You see, I didn't apply for the job here. I got sent.

LIZZIE: So?

RICHARD: Well, I mean, Singh has very powerful friends in Government.

LIZZIE:	So?
RICHARD:	Well, there's not much I can do, because if Singh inquires too closely with these people, these important people, they might let something drop.
LIZZIE:	Richard, I really don't understand you. What are you getting at?
RICHARD:	Now please, please treat this as highly confidential and personal.
LIZZIE:	Of course.
RICHARD:	It mustn't get out.
LIZZIE:	What is it?
	(RICHARD *takes out his black passbook and hands it over.*)
LIZZIE:	(*Stares at it.*) But, Richard, this is marvellous. I didn't know. I didn't guess.
RICHARD:	It is not marvellous. It's hell. You just can't imagine. All my life I've been able to cope. I got through school. I wasn't good at games but I got by. None of the other children knew and most of the teachers didn't know. Then I got through university – poring over articles pressed up to my face. Then my father got me into the Civil Service. And still nobody knew. I had an office on my own. Nobody could see me. I was competent, capable. I got promotion. Still nobody knew. Then I saw this file. The plan for the issue of passbooks. And still it wasn't me. But I got one. Through the post. The black book.
LIZZIE:	But Richard, there is nothing wrong with having a black book.
RICHARD:	Nothing wrong? You don't know what you're talking about. Do you think, for one minute, I'd have got promotion if they'd known?
LIZZIE:	But you got promotion to come here.

RICHARD:	Don't you understand anything? This is a dead end. I can't go back. I'm here now. And I can't tell anyone.
LIZZIE:	Why not?
RICHARD:	Because I sent everyone here. I pointed the finger. I said, 'It's to Aldershot for your own good, whether you like it or not.' Can you imagine what some of them will do to me?
LIZZIE:	God almighty, Richard. It's good to be here. This is where it's at. People love it here. People are proud to be here, they're proud of being people with disabilities. There is nothing to be ashamed of. Nothing. Richard, why do you hide it? Your eyesight is bad, so what? You're a competent administrator. Why lie about it? It's the reality. Why not face it?
RICHARD:	Lizzie, please don't tell anyone. Please, I'll never get out if people know. I told you in confidence. As a friend.
LIZZIE:	But why should you want to get out? This is the fulfilment of a dream. You said so yourself. Stop lying to yourself. Come out. Declare yourself.
RICHARD:	For God's sake, they'll crucify me if they find out. That's why I can do nothing about Singh.
LIZZIE:	God, you're spineless. You're worse than Singh.
RICHARD:	I told you as a friend. Please understand.

(Fade.)

(Back to Whitehall. The PM *is having a word with* MINISTER FOR DISABLED.)*

PM:	Now let me see, how's it all going?
MIN.:	Very well, ma'am.
PM:	I am a little concerned about the cost. It does seem higher than your original estimates. I really can't have that, you know. We must

watch the pennies, mustn't we?

MIN.: Oh, ma'am, I am very conscious of curtailing unnecessary expenditure. In fact, in my forthcoming visit, I will be outlining measures that significantly improve efficiency and slash costs.

PM: I am delighted to hear it. This repatriation scheme is going to cost enough and we must make savings wherever we can.

MIN.: Quite so, ma'am.

(Fade.)

(KARNY is sitting in her usual spot by the café. RICHARD enters. He carefully looks around, but doesn't see KARNY and takes out his magnifier to check a bus timetable. KARNY watches in fascination. Then the penny drops.)

KARNY: Oi, You! Jamieson! What you got there then?

RICHARD: I beg your pardon? Oh, Miss Jones, you made me start.

KARNY: Couldn't see me clearly then!

RICHARD: What do you mean? Of course. You just startled me.

KARNY: And what's that you put in your pocket? Looked suspiciously like a magnifier.

RICHARD: Don't be so ridiculous. And what if it was?

KARNY: Listen, man in a grey suit. I've seen enough partially sighted people to recognise a magnifier.

RICHARD: I don't know what you're talking about.

KARNY: And if you need a magnifier, you're partially sighted, and if you're partially sighted you need a precious black book. Don't you, Jamieson?

RICHARD: Don't be so ridiculous.

KARNY: Where's your black book, Mr Jamieson? Can't get in here without one, you know, Mr Jamieson. If you're disabled you get a black

	book. Bastard called Jamieson makes sure you have one.
RICHARD:	I'm not disabled.
KARNY:	Where's your black book, you hypocrite? Where's your bleedin' book? Pretending, were you? Won't be found out, eh? Well I have found out. Where's your sodding black book?
RICHARD:	Here! (*Thrusts book in* KARNY's *face.*) Satisfied?
	(KARNY *astounded and speechless.*)
	(*Fade.*)
	(*Enter* MINISTER FOR DISABLED. *He is to make a speech.* RICHARD *is alongside him, the rest of the company ranged in front.*)
MIN.:	It gives me great pleasure to see what was only a few months ago a dream, turn into the reality of this magnificent community. I have great pride in renaming the town that was the home of the British Army and now is the home of the British Handicapped, as Happiness Valley.
	(*Polite applause –* KARNY *blows a raspberry.*)
MIN.:	As I walk round the town, I can feel the happiness of people being with others similarly handicapped, having so much to share together.
KARNY:	Cobblers.
LIZZIE:	Minister, are you aware of the corruption in the administration of this community?
MIN.:	And I firmly believe that is only the start ... Corruption? That is a very serious accusation. But I know that any such unfortunate incidents will be investigated and the malefactors rooted out by Mr Jamieson.
LIZZIE:	But he won't, that's just the point.
MIN.:	I can assure you, Mr Jamieson has our full

confidence. I think it is, of course, totally understandable that there would be teething troubles at the start of such a new and magnificent concept. And of course, I am always happy to receive comments and ideas from residents of the community. (*To* RICHARD) Well, must be off now. I can leave you to read the latest measures, can't I? Three-line whip in the House, you know. (*Exit.*)

(RICHARD *draws an envelope from his pocket and takes out a document. Defiantly takes out his magnifier.*)

KARNY: There you are, blindy. Welcome to the club.

RICHARD: It is my responsibility as Resettlement Coordinator to implement policy changes arrived at by the Ministry. The Minister has left me specific instructions as follows.

KARNY: That's right, we've got to do what the a/bs want, ain't we?

RICHARD: In the first instance, the Ministry is aware of certain inconsistencies in the pay scales of workers in the sheltered employment provided. Everybody in such employment will in future be paid on strict piece rates.

LIZZIE: How the hell can the more severely handicapped people work as fast as others? That's pure discrimination. That's a scandal.

RICHARD: (*Carrying on, ignoring interruptions.*) Secondly, the Ministry is conscious of the need to protect the shift working of care attendants and wardens. A ten o'clock curfew will be put into effect as from tonight, and a compulsory lights out at ten thirty will similarly be enforced as from tonight.

LIZZIE: What? That's tyranny.

RICHARD: In future, weekend passes only will be issued to leave the settlement. Visitors will be requested to report to the main office on arriving at the settlement, and again on leaving.

KARNY: What did I tell you! *Stalag Luft* Valley. Bleedin' Nazis.

LIZZIE: Richard, please. You're one of us. You can't let this happen. You mustn't do it.

RICHARD: As Coordinator of Resettlement, it is my responsibility to carry out these policy decisions.

LIZZIE: Judas!

KARNY: Hypocrite! Bleedin' blindy.
(*Assorted ad lib abuse.*)

RICHARD: As Coordinator, it is my duty, it is my responsibility. I am a competent administrator, and this is my duty. I have to do it. I don't want to be here. It is my duty. I can cope. I'm here. I am the Coordinator. (*He breaks down.*)

Act III

(ROGER *crosses to what was* RICHARD's *desk and sits at it. He turns over the plaque. He reads:* 'R. Singh, Director, Resettlement Programme'. *He polishes it with care and satisfaction.*)

(*Fade.*)

(*Enter* LIZZIE, KARNY *and* YELDA.)

KARNY: They've even got you this time, Yelda. You haven't been out of the camp for ages.

YELDA: Well, dear, they keep changing the man on the gate and I never have time to get to know any of them well enough.

KARNY: You're losing your knack.

YELDA: Oh, I hope not, darling. That would be too

	demoralising.
LIZZIE:	I'm sure they're putting stuff in our food now. I just feel so tired all the time. I've got no energy. I just want to sleep. I haven't written anything for weeks. And Robert hasn't been down for ages.
KARNY:	I thought you two were splitting up anyway?
LIZZIE:	I thought so at one stage, but I was so involved with working here, that somehow it took up all my time and I didn't really have time to miss them.
YELDA:	How old is your baby now?
LIZZIE:	Oh, she's nearly four. I suppose I won't be able to get to her birthday. I wish they were here now.
YELDA:	There is this rumour, darlings, about sex.
LIZZIE:	What?
YELDA:	Sex. We're not supposed to have any.
KARNY:	(*Ironically*) Of course that will be a major change for me. But blimey, Yelda, what'll you do? No TV and now no sex, you're going to have to take up raffia mat making and hymn singing.
YELDA:	No, please don't mock, darling. If the rumour is true, it really is a bit alarming. I mean sex itself is OK, but only with other people here. You're not supposed to have it with outsiders. You know, able bodies.
KARNY:	(*Still not believing*) Go on, Yelda. Where does that leave you with the security men on the gate, eh?
YELDA:	An interesting point, sweetie. They're usually terribly enthusiastic. I can't imagine what'll become of the dears, if I don't visit them occasionally. But I suppose they are able bodies and so are simply beyond the pale.
LIZZIE:	You can't be serious, Yelda. That's

monstrous.

KARNY: Nothing new tho', is it? I mean they were sterilising mentally handicapped people in California, not so very long ago.

LIZZIE: I think I see the awakening of a political conscience.

KARNY: Now don't take the piss. But it does pay to see what's in the buggers' minds. Let's face it, handicap and sex have never actually received the royal assent.

YELDA: You're right, darling, more like a government health warning.

KARNY: Didn't stop you.

YELDA: Well, darling, I had to rise to the challenge, and it was so good for my tactile skills.

LIZZIE: But this is really terrible. I mean they surely can't impose on us to the extent of our personal lives.

KARNY: Where have you been, petal? Some of us didn't actually want to come here. Made no difference. We came. Same with other things. None of us wanted a curfew. So what?

YELDA: Well, darling, that's not absolutely one hundred per cent true. There are some who actually announced it, and there are some actually enforcing it.

LIZZIE: How can we get anywhere if we don't have solidarity? There is no group identity. No group consciousness. I mean, look at you two. Karny is only now thinking politically. I remember a time, Karny, when you discussed the rest of handicapped people as a bunch of cripples. And you made it very clear you weren't one.

KARNY: Yeah, well I got through the black bit, when I discovered that berk Jamieson was a proud possessor of a black book too.

LIZZIE: And you, Yelda, have never seen yourself as part of any group. But you've been forced to now.

YELDA: I suppose it looks like it, darling, force of circumstance and all, but I can't help feeling there is a way round it all.

KARNY: Oh yeah, like what?

YELDA: Well, darlings, let's look at what we all want.

KARNY: I want to get out.

YELDA: Yes, but you also want to be a rock star.

KARNY: I don't follow you.

LIZZIE: I want a political exposure of the corruption and oppression here.

YELDA: Well, one way would be to write articles, and another would be . . .

LIZZIE: To have a demonstration.

YELDA: Yes, and I just want to have the friends to do what I want to do.

KARNY: The problem with demos is that it'll give the likes of Singh the opportunity to crack down even more.

LIZZIE: The problem with rock groups is that it'll bring up the whole problem of disturbing the peace thing and get totally banned.

YELDA: I have a teeny idea, sweeties. I think Mr Singh, now he is such an important man, will be only too happy to develop a little project I fed him a few weeks ago.

KARNY: What's that?

YELDA: I'll tell you, darlings, when I've had a chat with the dusky Rajah.

      (Fade.)

  (ROGER's *office. He is on the phone to the Minister.*)

ROGER: No, Minister, everything is very quiet here. There was an original overload on the medical department, but we have everybody tranquillised now, so I don't foresee any major problems. The new Immorality Act will be brought into effect quite soon. But I think it is almost irrelevant as nobody has the energy. Oh, yes, I quite understand, Minister, it is an important plank in the overall philosophy of the Government. Yes, Minister. Look forward to your visit. Goodbye, Minister.

(*Puts phone down and reaches for microphone. This is the radio link to broadcast to all the community. Echo effects of some sort needed.*)

ANNOUNCER: We interrupt Radio Happiness Valley to bring you a message from Resettlement Director, Roger Singh.

ROGER: Good morning, Happiness Valley. You will be delighted to hear that the Government has expressed its overwhelming enthusiasm for the work being done here. As a direct result, unemployment has fallen dramatically and industrial output has accordingly risen. Furthermore, our brave boys in Northern Ireland are entirely in control of the domestic population, with the result that terrorism has been totally eradicated. Never let it be said that disabled people do not make a full and meaningful contribution to the welfare of the state as a whole.

(*Fade.*)

(KARNY *and* LIZZIE *are alone.* RICHARD *wanders in. He is totally out to lunch as a result of taking umpteen tranquillisers.*)

KARNY: Oh, look what the cat dragged in.

LIZZIE: Shut up, Karny. He's still not well. Sit down Richard. How are you?

RICHARD: Oh fine. Fine. Thank you.

LIZZIE: For God's sake, Karny, the man's ill.

KARNY: Maybe, but I remember only too well who

	sent me here, and how he treated me.
LIZZIE:	That doesn't make it right for you to continue putting the boot in. He was doing what he thought he had to do.
KARNY:	He was doing what he was doing, because he was too bloody scared to do anything else.
LIZZIE:	Maybe, but we're all scared of something.
RICHARD:	I don't think I recall who you . . .
KARNY:	I'm Karny Jones, Karny. You know the rock star in the attic.
RICHARD:	Karny – oh yes, I think.
KARNY:	God, he's as high as a kite. You should be a rock star, mate. Go down well with the bands, being as laid back as that, my old son.
LIZZIE:	Richard, you mustn't take those pills. You're out on your feet.
KARNY:	In this dump, that's an advantage.
LIZZIE:	Karny, come on. Whatever you think of Richard it's not right that he lives the rest of his life like a zombie.
KARNY:	I dunno. I think I prefer him this way. All right, all right. I'll help. Come on, Richard. You've got to start walking, me old mate.
LIZZIE:	And coffee.
KARNY:	And coffee. God, this is going to be tedious. What do you do with your pills, then?
LIZZIE:	Flush them. I still think they put something in the food, though.
KARNY:	Well, we'd all better walk so we're nice and fresh for Yelda and her great scheme. Come on, get moving.

(Fade.)

(ROGER's *office.*)

ROGER:	Ah, Yelda, what a welcome surprise. I was thinking I had done something to make you avoid me.
YELDA:	Why, Rajah darling, you are now so important that I just walk in awe, and felt

	you'd be far too busy to see little me.
ROGER:	I'm never too busy to see you, my dear. Now, what can I do for you?
YELDA:	Dear Rajah, you're so considerate. It's only about that boring little idea connected with the Singh Performing Arts Centre.
ROGER:	Oh yes, I remember. Splendid idea. I'm sure we were thinking of another name, though.
YELDA:	You had a simply super brainwave to call it the Courage Centre.
ROGER:	Of course, of course.
YELDA:	Well I was thinking, in my silly way, that it would be super to do a sort of show. You know, about Happiness Valley. If we got something off the ground and there's a lot of talent, maybe we could tour it round other settlements, and then take it to the big cities.
ROGER:	That's very interesting. I must think about that. Now, what sort of show?
YELDA:	Well I was thinking, a sort of revue. You know, give people a chance to display their talents.
ROGER:	Mmmm. Yes, I like that. Now you'll need a compère, master of ceremonies, of course.
YELDA:	We were thinking of holding auditions, you know?
ROGER:	I was just wondering. As the main benefactor, it would be appropriate for me to, as it were, host the evening, don't you think?
YELDA:	Ah. Well, Rajah, what a lovely idea, but I'm sure you're far too busy with really important things to spare the time.
ROGER:	Oh no, no, no. I'm sure I can fit in the odd rehearsal. It's settled then. It also saves you time for auditioning. Splendid idea. I look forward to starting work, and I'll get my building contractors to look at an

appropriate design for the building.

YELDA: (*Doubtful*) Oh, good.

      (*Fade.*)

(KARNY *and* LIZZIE *are still walking* RICHARD. *They stop.* RICHARD *slumps down.*)

KARNY: Right, what's your name?

RICHARD: Richard, Richard Jamieson.

KARNY: Louder.

RICHARD: Richard Jamieson.

KARNY: Louder.

RICHARD: Richard Jamieson.

LIZZIE: Where do you live?

RICHARD: 34, Firs Avenue, Sutton.

KARNY: Where do you live now?

RICHARD: 189b, Douglas Bader Avenue, Happiness Valley.

KARNY: How old are you?

RICHARD: Thirty-two.

LIZZIE: What do you do?

RICHARD: Street cleaner.

KARNY: What did you do?

RICHARD: I was, er . . .

KARNY: Yes?

RICHARD: I was Resettlement Coordinator.

KARNY: What?

RICHARD: Resettlement Coordinator.

KARNY: Your passbook number?

RICHARD: N104732.

KARNY: Louder.

RICHARD: N104732.

KARNY: Louder.

RICHARD: N104732.

LIZZIE: Handicap?

RICHARD: Weak vision.

KARNY: That's not what it says.

RICHARD: Partially sighted.

KARNY: What?

RICHARD: Partially sight . . .

LIZZIE:	What?
KARNY:	

RICHARD: Partially sighted.

KARNY: Welcome to the club, sunbeam.

                    (*Fade.*)

(ROGER's *office – on phone again.*)

ROGER: I'm glad you like my idea, Minister. I think we can look forward to very positive publicity. You will? Oh that's marvellous. That would be a great honour. An event I'm sure the valley would remember always. A great honour. You'll be in touch. Thank you sir, thank you. (*He stands up – bows and greets imaginary dignitary.*) Your Majesty, such an honour. (*He then drops to one knee and assumes female voice.*) Arise, Sir Rajah. (*He fails to get up.*) Arise, Sir Rajah. (*Grunts and groans – eventually makes it.*)

                    (*Fade.*)

(YELDA *has returned.* LIZZIE, KARNY *and* RICHARD *listen.*)

YELDA: So, darlings, we do a show. Get lots of publicity, lots of money, tour round the country, maybe abroad, won't it be lovely?

LIZZIE: Yes, but they won't let us do what we want to do.

KARNY: What you want to do, you mean.

LIZZIE: But this is the opportunity to get through to the outside world. To let them know what it's really like. Don't you see?

KARNY: Yeah, but they won't fund that sort of thing.

YELDA: You may have a point there. The bad news, my dear, is that Roger Singh most definitely wants to be compère.

LIZZIE: He can't just demand that.

YELDA: Well, darling, he is putting up the loot, isn't he?

LIZZIE:	Shit!
KARNY:	So what sort of show can we do, then?
RICHARD:	What if we do two shows? One for Singh, a nice light revue. And then the real one that we spring on the night.
KARNY:	Blimey, you've come off them pills, ain't you?
LIZZIE:	But won't Singh smell a rat?
YELDA:	I think that sounds a lovely idea.
KARNY:	Yeah, but as soon as we sock them with the real show, we'll never get out. They won't let us tour a show that blows the lid off Happiness Death Camp.
YELDA:	True, dear.
LIZZIE:	So what do we do, play by their rules and get what we want – that is, the chance to get out? Or do what we believe in and run the risk of never getting out of here and never getting people to see the show?
ANNOUNCER: (*on tannoy*)	Would you stand by for an announcement from the Director of Resettlement Services.
ROGER: (*on tannoy*)	I have much pride in announcing that the newly developed Performing Arts Centre is to be officially opened by Her Majesty the Queen as the Courage Arts Centre. Her Majesty has graciously accepted an invitation to attend the opening performance by the Courage Players. This will take the form of a revue, exhibiting the talents of the inhabitants of Happiness Valley. People interested in performing should contact me, Roger Singh, at the main office. Thank you.
LIZZIE:	Right, that's it. If the Queen's going to be there, then so are all the Government representatives. At least we can show them what we feel. It's the only chance we have of getting them to change their minds. I go for Richard's idea.

YELDA: Well, dears, I'm not so sure. Will it really change anything?

KARNY: I think Lizzie's right, we've got to give it a go.

RICHARD: I agree.

YELDA: Oh, all right then. You'd better concoct some agreeable little offerings for Singh, and we'll get together for the alternative show.

LIZZIE: Right. We'll sock them between the eyes!
                        (*Fade*.)

              (YELDA, RICHARD, KARNY *and* LIZZIE *are preparing for a final rehearsal*.)

YELDA: Darling, we're expecting Rajah Singh any moment now. He wants to see our little offering.

              (ROGER *enters. Various greetings*.)

ROGER: Hello, hello, everybody.

YELDA: Now, dear Roger, I'm sure you're going to love this, isn't he? Now do you know everyone? This is Richard Jamieson – oh, of course you know him, don't you. This is Karny Jones. Oh, you've met her, haven't you? And Lizzie Baxter? Well isn't that lovely? Everybody knows everybody.

ROGER: I'm really looking forward to this. I've been looking up some old jokes.

KARNY: I can believe that.

ROGER: Pardon?

KARNY: I've always found you very funny, Mr Singh.

ROGER: Oh good.

LIZZIE: We do hope we'll bring a little light into people's lives.

ROGER: My sentiments exactly.

RICHARD: As you see, Mr Singh, we're all braced and ready to go.

ROGER: Marvellous. Now let me see ... On the programme you, Richard, are doing a recitation. That's very cultural. Am I going to see that now?

YELDA: Well no, darling. We actually thought we'd do for you the opening song. I think you'll find it awfully uplifting. Sort of catchy tune. Lizzie wrote it. Very talented.

ROGER: Oh, tremendous.

YELDA: Let's get to our places, darlings. Ready? Here we go then. One, two, three, four.

SONG

KARNY ⎫
LIZZIE ⎬   Go down the M3 Motorway
RICHARD ⎭   Turn off at Junction 4
               You're en route for Happiness Valley
               The ever open door
               Roll down in your wheelchair
               Or travel in an adapted bus
               But come down to Happiness Valley
               It's the place for us.
               (*As they sing, they smile at the audience.*)

ROGER: Oh jolly good. Marvellous, Lizzie.

YELDA: Next verse, sweetie. One, two, three, four.

KARNY ⎫
LIZZIE ⎬   Join us in Happiness Valley
RICHARD ⎭   If your eyesight's growing dim
               If your hearing is pretty ropey
               Or you've gone and lost a limb
               Here in Happiness Valley
               All your dreams come true
               No more steps and no more pavements
               And no inaccessible loo.

YELDA: Last verse, sweeties.

KARNY ⎫
LIZZIE ⎬   Here the sun is always shining
RICHARD ⎭   And the sky is always blue
               Lots of friends we have to talk with
               There's always lots to do
               So roll down the M3 Motorway

And turn off at Junction 4
Here in Happiness Valley
There's always room for more.

ROGER: Marvellous, marvellous. Oh congratu-
              lations, congratulations. Lizzie, such wit.
              Oh, I'm so happy. Dear Yelda, that was
              marvellous, marvellous.

YELDA: So glad you liked it, darling.

ROGER: Oh, I'm so looking forward to the show.
              Keep up the good work. Break a leg,
              puncture a tyre. (*Exit.*)

KARNY: Break your neck.

YELDA: Well, I think we've cracked it, sweetie.

RICHARD: Certainly looks like it.

KARNY: God, when the bastard hears the real thing,
              he's going to shit his pants.

YELDA: Darlings, let's go somewhere private and
              rehearse our other offering.

RICHARD: My place then. Cocoa.

YELDA: That's lovely. Let's go, darlings. (*Exeunt*)
                          (*Fade.*)

              (*The opening of the Courage Centre:* ROGER *is
              dressed in full flash evening number – he goes to
              greet the* QUEEN.)

ROGER: Your Majesty, this is such a great honour.
              Your Majesty, this way. Be careful, Your
              Majesty. Is Your Majesty quite comfy?

QUEEN: We are very happy to be here. We are very
              happy to be here.

MIN. FOR   Jolly good show, Singh. Everything running
DISABLED   smoothly? Excellent, excellent.

MIN. FOR   Jolly good show, Singh. Everything running
EMPLOYMENT: smoothly? Excellent, excellent.

PM: Oh do shut up, you two. Jolly good show,
              Singh, everything running smoothly?
              Excellent. Excellent.

ROGER: Thank you, ma'am, honoured sirs. Now this

way, Your Majesty. A little quiet, please.

QUEEN: It is a great honour and privilege to come tonight to see the strides that have been made, or should I say the wheels that have turned – Ha! Ha! – (*sycophantic laughter from* SINGH) to culminate in this magnificent, nearly completed, accessible building. I know this evening we will have demonstrated to us beyond any doubt that the disabled are as talented as the rest of us. I have great pleasure in naming this building the Courage Centre for Performing Arts by the Disabled. Thank you.

ROGER: Three cheers for Her Majesty. Hip, hip . . . And now, ladies and gentlemen – welcome to our evening's entertainment. We hope to establish an annual event that will be honoured, as we are tonight, by the presence of a Royal Person, and will be entitled a Royal Disabled Command Show. And now to this evening's entertainment. I am your host and my name is Roger Singh. I was hoping to sing, but the rest of the company didn't want to be associated with Sing Sing. (*Waits for laugh.*) My oh my, we are slow tonight. Let me tell you about the one-legged man who tried to get on a full bus. The conductor told him to 'hop it'. Get it! Well, enough of this, and let's get on to the real business. As you see from our programme, there is a wide range of acts, including wheelchair dancing and the massed choir of Happiness Valley. But we start with a solo, performed by a lovely lady, which I am sure sums up the feelings of everybody gathered here – 'We shall overcome'.

(*Spots on* KARNY. *She sings.*)

KARNY'S SONG

KARNY: People's minds are locked
           In narrow steel straight lines
           Nothing ever changes
           No diversion signs

           Messy little problems
           Need neat and tidy holes
           Pop them in, forget them
           Sunlight's not for moles—

CHORUS: *Niggers, wops and spics*
           They've all felt your bricks
           And now it's the turn
           Of the filthy little crips

KARNY: Sewage runs away
           Far beneath your feet
           Out of sight and out of smell
           It's nicer when you eat

           Channels underground
           Full of filth and shit
           Carefully covered over
           In case you stand in it

           (CHORUS)

           It's the same with people
           Shove us out the way
           Put us in cold storage
           And there we're going to stay

           Dump us in the ghetto
           Garbage on the heap
           Bogeys come to frighten
           Little children from their sleep

168 *Disability, Theatre and Education*

(CHORUS)

(*Enter* ROGER *at end of song.*)

ROGER: Your Majesty, ladies and gentlemen. What can I say? I am appalled. I had no idea. My humble apologies.
(*Pause.*)

QUEEN: I thought it was rather good. Interesting point of view.

PM: Yes. Full of original thinking.

MIN. FOR DISABLED: Just the sort of things I've been saying for years, give the people a jolt.

ALL: Jolly good. (*Applause.*)
(KARNY *looks amazed, then triumphant.* RICHARD, YELDA *and* LIZZIE *come on and congratulate her.* PM *and* MINISTERS *face front.*)

PM: Happiness Valley is a success. Three new centres opening.

MIN. FOR EMPLOYMENT: Employment drastically reduced. New Commonwealth citizens to be repatriated.

MIN. FOR THE DISABLED: Voluntary sterilisation of disabled people to be encouraged by grants to volunteers.

QUEEN: We have so much to learn from the less than fortunate. Their courage is a byword. We can measure how civilised a country we are by our policies towards our disabled members. We can hold our heads high in this country, can't we?

THE END

7: Odds and Ends

This is a ragbag chapter, gathering together various points that have not been discussed so far. It is also an attempt to satisfy some of the questions that follow most performances.

1. *Graeae – what does it mean?*
In our search for a name for the company we went through a host of possibilities. Of one thing we were certain, we did not wish the words 'handicap' or 'disability' to figure. We are still bedevilled by publicity departments who go to the lengths of calling us the Graeae Disabled Theatre Company. The *Observer* colour supplement, while paying us the great compliment of doing a feature article on us, undermined our elation by entitling the piece 'The Theatre of the Disabled'.

We looked for appropriate classical names to adopt. 'Cyclops' was an obvious possibility; so was 'Hephæstus' who was the Greek god of fire, crippled by being knocked from Mount Olympus by his father, Zeus, as a punishment for taking his mother's side. Hephæstus made his own leg irons so that he could walk, but apparently he was still a dwarfish, grotesque figure, frequently the butt of godly humour. He would have been ideal, except that there was a special school outside Reading that also used his name.

In the back of Nabil's mind there was a classical story concerning three old women who shared between them an eye and a tooth which they passed round. He seemed to remember that they were something to do with Medusa who turned people to stone by her look. On checking this, he found that there were indeed three such old ladies, who, after he had

stolen the eye from them, were forced to divulge to the Greek
hero Perseus how he might dispose of Medusa. He was
instructed to polish his shield and use it as a mirror, slaying her
without looking directly on her face, and this he duly did. The
three old ladies were the Graeae. The story appealed to both of
us and we were happy to concoct morals on the subject of
disabled people helping each other or of never letting able-
bodied people pinch your eye from you. But the real reason
why the name was chosen was because we both liked it. We
pronounce it 'Grey-eye', although technically the first syllable
should rhyme with the second.

2. *What do you do for money?*

When we first started performances in April, 1980, we had no
money at all and relied upon individuals' contributions to get
about. We were donated some money to buy letter headings
and stamps, but it was only when we started earning from box
office that we managed to start covering our costs.

   The American trip was sponsored by the generosity of the
John Silver Trust Fund and the University of Illinois. Even so
each member of the company took with him some £200 for
personal expenses. The post-American tour was funded out of
box office receipts. Only on the making of a documentary for
the BBC 2 programme 'Arena' were people actually paid more
than expenses.

   The establishment of a full-time company in June, 1981, put
far more of a burden on our financial management. We had
received incredibly generous donations, including a set of
prints from the artist Peter Blake. But it is disconcerting how
quickly funds can be dissipated when one is attempting to pay
Equity minimum salaries. The company was much helped by
having its administration in the hands of Rhombus Production
Services, a full-time professional administrative company.

   However, the financial history of Graeae has shown us
lurching from crisis to crisis. To exist on box office and private
donations is practically impossible for a fringe company. The
problem that confronted Graeae was that to get going properly
it needed a subsidy, but no funding body would offer one

unless it could see what Graeae had to offer. We were not another fringe company with experienced and established performers, but a group of people who were new and untried. Funding bodies have offered us much encouragement, but in its first year of trading the company has been at a serious financial disadvantage. I know of no other approach we could have taken. If we had waited for proper funding we would still be waiting. I would not recommend this course of action to anyone seeking peace of mind, but in the end we all felt that we had to do it and accept the risks.

3. *What are the problems of touring?*

I have described some of them in previous chapters. It is no good pretending that touring with Graeae is exactly the same as with any other touring company. In many ways it is, but at the same time considerable onus is placed upon the able-bodied members of the company to offer personal help. Having toured with only a director and a stage manager acting in a multitude of capacities, we recognise that another person, whose main responsibility is the care of the company, is essential. One might describe this post as a company manager who would check on accommodation and, for example, on the accessibility of bathrooms, and who would help generally as well as assist in driving. This post would alleviate a lot of the work at present shared between the stage manager, actors and director, whose prime responsibilities lie elsewhere.

Transport is another constant problem. Initially we bought an old social services ambulance which had a tailgate lift. This was less than an ideal vehicle, as it rattled appallingly and only did about 50 mph at best. None the less, the company travelled up to Edinburgh in it for the 1981 Festival. Unfortunately the van eventually died, and the company has had to improvise or hire, preferring to travel by train for long trips. The only problem connected with this is loading and unloading the props and costumes, as well as the performers. There have been occasions when obstructive station staff have almost succeeded in leaving the whole company on the platform. On one occasion it was only the intervention of the train driver himself that allowed all the props to be loaded. Usually, of course, station staff are extremely helpful, although there does seem to be a perennial communication breakdown whereby, no matter how far in advance a station is advised of Graeae's travel plans, the station staff on the day know nothing of them.

4. *What do you do about illness?*
This seems to afflict Graeae no more frequently than any other company. Marion Saunders played several shows with the mumps, as did Nabil with chicken-pox. The only major problem was when Will Kennen had an epileptic seizure just before a performance. This only happened once, and on that occasion I explained the situation to the audience and stood in. Nic has had to do the same, but it is very rare.

One of the original full-time company, Mike Flower, has multiple sclerosis. He found the travel and the pressure of frequent performances extremely exhausting. As it was adversely affecting his health he decided to call it a day, after a month. This experience must make us think very carefully and ask many more questions before employing somebody with a similar disability. But then, both Marion Saunders and Ellen Wilkie, who have muscular dystrophy, reputedly an extremely debilitating condition, stood up extremely well to touring. Given that in the period between June and December 1981 the company gave over a hundred performances at sixty-one different venues, stamina would seem not to be a major problem.

5. *Where do company members come from and how do you recruit them?*
Company members come from all over and from a wide variety of backgrounds. Virtually none of them has had any theatrical experience and most have very limited knowledge of the hierarchies and traditions of theatre. On the one hand it was infuriating to find that the Edinburgh Festival meant virtually nothing to most of the company, but on the other it is refreshing to find a theatre group who are totally unsophisticated as far as the relative importance of the various

venues is concerned. For a part-time fringe theatre company to start its tour in June and within five months to find itself the subject of a fifty-minute documentary on BBC 2 and playing at the Riverside Studios, is nothing less than breathtaking. Graeae took it all in its stride.

The company was recruited in the conventional way by holding auditions. The definition of disability has occasioned various amusing telephone conversations. Once a potential auditioner rang up, saying he was from New Zealand, and was that enough of a handicap? I could only reply that usually I would consider it so, but unfortunately he had to do a little better for Graeae.

Graeae has had changes in personnel since it became a full-time company. Three of the original part-time group became founder members of the professional one. One of those, Nabil Shaban, has since left, and there have been three other members, including Mike Flower, mentioned above, who left because of illness. Any future company might well have a core of two or three experienced performers and be supplemented by new recruits. There has been a change in stage management, Mandy Sprague being replaced by Sue Bishop. Nic Fine has been director since the establishment of the full-time group.

6. *Where are you based?*
Finding a rehearsal space was a tremendous problem initially. Again, generosity from various individuals allowed us to develop *Sideshow*. It was only when we played at the West End Centre, Aldershot, that we had the opportunity of a permanent base. Jem Barnes, the Director, offered us a 'no strings' deal comprising a rehearsal base and attached office, with use of workshop, printing and costume-making facilities. This was a tremendously generous offer and the company has been happily based there ever since.

However, the associated problem to finding a base – finding appropriate accommodation – has proved far more of a headache. A disabled person is far more restricted in his choice of suitable living space. The only real and permanent answer is to have hostel accommodation actually attached to the rehearsal centre. In the meantime people either have to travel or put up with less than satisfactory digs.

7. *What special costumes, props and sets are needed?*

At times, when individuals have had difficulty in lifting or manipulating something, it has been necessary to make special props. Ellen, for example, does not have the strength to pull the trigger of a toy gun. It was necessary to make a sound effect off stage.

If a costume change on stage is called for, as in *Sideshow*, a single tug can quickly remove garments, because they are all fitted with velcro fastening. Yvonne, Ellen and Marion have at times had problems removing costumes, but usually because they have become caught in the wheels of their chairs.

Elane has always had particular problems in finding her way round the stage. A raised stage presents a danger because she cannot see the edge, and this has been resolved by putting down a length of foot-wide rubber matting about six inches from the edge. She has always, to date, played barefoot and so knows as soon as she strays too near the edge, by the texture underfoot. This, of course, has not stopped her walking into fellow performers or objects on stage. On one occasion she walked off a raised stage and, forgetting that the platform in the wings was narrow, stepped into space. I was on stage at the time and all I heard was a thud followed by a suppressed giggle. At least that told me that she was unhurt.

The same performance was memorable for another incident directly related to Elane's blindness. One scene of the show had the actors throwing sweets into the audience. Elane did this with the others, although never knowing where the sweets would land. She threw long and hard. About half-way back on a raised platform sat a harmless little old lady in a wheelchair. I could see from the stage that Elane's sweet was travelling with unnerving accuracy towards this lady. She, needless to say, had not seen it. It caught her neatly between the eyes, resulting in an anguished cry and a severe spasm. Everybody on stage could see this and was convulsed with laughter. Of course,

Elane had no idea what had happened until it could be explained to her after the show. However, such is her composure and skill on stage that it has always come as a surprise to audiences to find out after the show that she is, indeed, blind.

8. *What sort of relationship does Graeae have with the media?*
Most of the company would argue that the media have been conspicuous in their inability to depict disability positively. Articles and TV coverage of disabled people's activities tend to play up the 'courageous' aspects rather than the skills being displayed. Graeae has had its fair share of misrepresentation and misinterpretation. I have already mentioned the *Observer*'s use of the term 'Theatre of the Disabled'. Other journalists' attempts have also met with criticism. Elane was annoyed at a reference to her as a 'beautiful blind dancer'. She took exception to the juxtaposition of the words 'blind' and 'beautiful' as if they had some special significance by being associated. This sort of reaction may seem pedantic, and yet the clumsy use of words in describing people with disability can only reinforce the negative connotations.

It has been suggested that there are two ways of looking at disability. The first is the traditional way of seeing a person succumbing to a disability and allowing it to dominate every aspect of his own and his immediate family's lives. The other is to see disability as a part of life that has to be coped with. It is aggravating and in certain situations profoundly handicapping, but it is not all-pervading.

The Press find it very hard to make this distinction. The newsworthy story is the one that centres on the disability. Graeae, of course, has made great capital out of this on the precept that all publicity is good publicity.

Television coverage presents similar problems. Usually news magazine programmes have little time to reflect. The camera crew gets in, takes the footage and gets out. It's a smash and grab operation with little attempt to consider how disability might be portrayed positively. At other times the company have been hired to perform scenes which have been entirely inappropriate for the mood of the programme. Recently a 'God slot' programme on courage (of course) used Graeae as an example. The excerpt shown was of the song 'One for the cripple coming through the door', which totally debunks patronising attitudes. The message of the song was completely missed by the programme makers, who found the succumbing image of disability far more powerful. Disability, and not the company's talent for satire, had been the reason for hiring them.

This and other experiences have made Graeae extremely cautious of doing TV work. One either has to take the cynical view that the pay is good, or one has to enter into a far more cooperative relationship with the film makers. This was the group's intention when approached by Heather Mansfield of Feather Productions with a proposal to make some programmes to sell to the Fourth Channel. The huge number of meetings and telephone calls that this project engendered was perhaps inevitable, since the two parties had aims that were not always identical and methods that could clash. In the one week's shooting for the pilot film we found that film crews stop and start a lot, and that theatre companies ramble on, setting great store by flow. The two approaches could easily become incompatible, and so a very close and honest debate is essential right the way through the shooting.

An even greater opportunity for disagreement and misunderstanding is the editing period. Editing is, of course, a professional skill, and it is very hard for inexperienced actors to know what will and what will not work. A lengthy debate on how disability should be portrayed, accompanied by some degree of understanding, is essential. The actors have to trust the film makers, as well as vice versa.

In Chapter 2 I discussed how Graeae has reached its decisions on the theatrical use of disability. That discussion has to be extended to include other media. The underlying principle, as I have said, is that actors with disabilities should be seen as coping with their disabilities, rather than succumbing to them. That theoretical distinction is much harder to put into practice. But it must always be at the forefront of our thinking in any project that seeks to display disability in a public manner.

9. *What is Graeae going to do next?*

This is the 64,000-dollar question. After *Sideshow* we had no real idea; the same was true after *3D*; we are in the same position now that we have completed *M3 Junction 4*. The shows are very different and do indicate some progression of thought. Maybe we shall get round to performing some of the alternatives I discussed in Chapter 5. Maybe a new company will throw up a completely different perspective. I think that for the short-term future we will be developing our own material, still, hopefully, with a writer in residence. Perhaps we will embark on mixed productions, using both able-bodied and disabled performers. In the fullness of time I have no doubt that we will try work by established authors. I look forward to Graeae's production of *Macbeth* but I suspect it will be some time yet.

The workshops and the training programmes will continue and it may be that the company will split itself in two – one half to pursue the theatre-in-education role and the other to concentrate on performing plays.

Ultimately, one might argue, the Graeae Theatre Company will go out of business only when disabled performers have as much chance of gaining admission to drama schools and acting courses, and hence to work, as anyone else. I think this is wishful thinking: indeed, it might weaken the unique contribution that disabled people can bring to performance.

Conclusion

Graeae's philosophy and its performances have been criticised by some disabled people, who have argued that the company furthers the ghetto image of disability, or that it rocks the boat, or that it is irrelevant. I have been attacked for writing about disability although I am not disabled. One should be glad that disabled people (who are, after all, people like everyone else – a fact often overlooked) as well as able-bodied, have their prejudices and opinions. It would be far more disturbing if

Graeae received universal support from everyone. We have always encouraged disabled people to offer scripts, and I hope that one will take over the job of writer in residence, as it is a fascinating and demanding task. I do, however, reject the idea that only a disabled person has the insight or the skill to write good plays about disability. I also reject the idea that disabled actors will necessarily play disabled characters on stage better than able-bodied actors. They will only do so if they are better writers or better actors. What Graeae aims to do is offer the writers and actors the chance to learn the skills and techniques, so that they can improve. In the end, Graeae will have succeeded if more disabled people can put on their passports the word 'actor' or 'writer', in the knowledge that not only is the description accurate but that they have the experience, expertise and opportunity to prove it.

Appendices

Further Reading
It is very difficult to make suggestions for further reading, as books tend to fall into one of two camps – either those exclusively devoted to theatre and drama, or those on physical handicap.

However there have been publications which have helped me refine my thinking. On the theatre side Athol Fugard's comments on the role of the actor, in his Introduction to a collection of his plays, *Statements: Three Plays*, (O.U.P., 1974) is full of insight. Jerzy Grotowski's *Towards a Poor Theatre* (Simon & Schuster, 1976) also has many important and valuable things to say about acting related to reality. It was a relief in reading this book to see observations made by a master reflecting and being of relevance to one's own experience. Peter Brooks' *The Empty Space* is a seminal work, but of more interest to me was an account of a group of actors led by Brooks travelling through Africa, entitled *The Conference of the Birds*, John Heilpern (Penguin, 1978). What he has to say about the meaning of a journey and the meaning of communication seems relevant to Graeae's development. *M3 Junction 4* was very much inspired by the as yet unpublished play, *Woza Albert*, which I saw at the Riverside Studios, Hammersmith, in 1982.

On the subject of handicap, I have found Beatrice Wright's book *Physical Disability – A Psychological Approach* (Harper & Row, 1960) an invaluable goad to my thinking. Although published more than twenty years ago, it has many important and profoundly relevant things to say. Jo Campling's book on disabled women, *Images of Ourselves: Women with Disabilities Talking* (Routledge & Kegan Paul, 1981) gave me many varied insights into the relationship that a disabled woman has with her body. Wendy Greengross' *Entitled to Love* (Malady Press, 1976) similarly throws open windows on a disabled person's sexuality. Erving Goffman's *Stigma: Notes on the Management of Spoiled Identity* (Penguin, 1968) encourages a review of one's attitudes towards any minority group.

However, the main source of inspiration and influence since 1972 has undoubtedly been the people who have told me their stories and given me their opinions. The real experience has an impact that no amount of theorising and intellectual analysis can match.

Chronology

1971–72	Revues and poetry readings at Hereward College of Further Education, Coventry.
1972–75	A variety of productions at the above college, including: *Everyman* *The Dumb Waiter* (Pinter) *Schoolplay* (Howarth) *Never Mind, You'll Soon Get Better* *Ready Salted Crips*
1976	*Sideshow* first performed at the University of Illinois, U.S.A.
1979, Aug.	First workshops to assess interest in a company.
1980, Feb.	Company auditions and first rehearsals.
April	First performance of *Sideshow* at the University of Surrey
June	Tour of Illinois, U.S.A., and Winnipeg, Canada
Aug.	Start of tour in England
Nov.	Filming for BBC2 *Arena*
1981, Jan.	Performance for a week at the Riverside Studios, Hammersmith, of *Sideshow*. Screening of *Arena* film *Getting Away from Sydney*
May	Founding of full time, professional company
Aug.	Performance at the Edinburgh Festival of a new show entitled *3D*
Aug.–Dec.	Extensive touring throughout the country – over one hundred performances in sixty venues.
1982, Jan.	Touring recommences.
Feb.	Filming of pilot programme for the Fourth Channel.
May	Opening of new show *M3 Junction 4* in Sheffield
May 29th	Company temporarily disbanded to review its financial situation, with the objective of restarting in September.

Index